Domesticated Ducks & Geese

The International Poultry Library is believed to be the largest Series of books on poultry-keeping in the world. It covers a wide range of subjects for the fancier and the farmer. Readers will be supplied with a comprehensive list on request (a large, stamped addressed envelope would be appreciated).

For a *Companion Title* covering fancy waterfowl (semi-wild birds kept on a pond) readers are referred to:

FANCY WATERFOWL, FRANK FINN

DOMESTICATED DUCKS
&
GEESE

JOSEPH BATTY

Beech Publishing House

First Edition 1979
Second Edition 1985
Third Impression 1994
Third Edition (revised) 1996

ISBN 1-85736-091-8

<u>British Library Cataloguing-in-Publication Data</u>
A catalogue record for this book is available from the
British Library.

Beech Publishing House
Station Yard
Elsted
Midhurst GU29 0JT

Printed in Malta by Interprint Limited.

ACKNOWLEDGEMENTS

In writing a book of this kind, covering so many breeds of ducks and geese, it has been essential to consult a number of fanciers. In particular, I acknowledge the assistance given by the following persons or organizations who supplied advice and/or photographs.

Anita-Dawn Allen, Ash Tree Farm, Old Ditch, Westbury-sub-Mendip, Nr. Wells, Somerset.

Group Captain Leslie Bonnet, Ymwlch Fawr, Criccieth, Gwynedd, Wales.

British Waterfowl Association, Market Place, Haltwhistle, Northumberland.

George H. Elt Ltd., Eltex Works, Worcester.

Mrs. Lorna Heard, Bank Farm, Wilton, Marlborough, Wiltshire.

Charles and Maggie Piper, Keepers Cottage, Alford Acre, Alford, Castle Cary, Somerset.

Poultry World, Surrey House, 1 Throwley Way, Sutton, Surrey.

Mrs. Barbara Soames, Fordgate Cottage, Heatree Cross, Manaton, Newton Abbot, Devon.

Vandyck Studios, 26 Alexandra Road, Farnborough, Hampshire.

Dr. A.F. Anderson Brown, author of *The Incubation Book*, Blundeston Hall, Lowestoft, Suffolk.

Sketches and/or drawings were compiled by **Miss Rosemary Towler** and **Miss Amanda-Jane Wood**.

In addition, a number of out of print books were used for reference, particularly on the rare breeds.

Liss,   J. BATTY
Hants.

WEIGHT CONVERSION TABLE

Imperial Measurement	Metric Measurement
lb	*kg*
4	1.814
5	2.268
6	2.722
7	3.175
8	3.629
9	4.082
10	4.536
11	4.990
12	5.443
13	5.897
14	6.350
15	6.804
16	7.258
17	7.711
18	8.165
19	8.618
20	9.072

CONTENTS

     COLOUR PLATES: Ducks
     Geese

LOYALTY: The Blind Woman & the Gander
It has been recorded that many years ago in Germany a gander would
lead a blind woman to church and back.

INTRODUCTION

In writing this book I do so purely as an amateur who has kept some varieties of duck and geese but, sadly, not all. My wife has also kept waterfowl intermittently over a number of years and takes delight in rearing them as a hobby.

We have received many requests for a concise and yet comprehensive book on *domesticated* ducks and geese. The waterfowl side is already covered in a number of books, and the reader looking for information on these beautiful birds is referred to *Ornamental Waterfowl* (A.A. Johnson and W.H. Payn

Many more suitable authors no doubt could have been found, but those approached were not able to find the time or perhaps, in modesty, felt they were not able to do justice to a rather difficult task.

In putting together the contents of these pages I have called upon the advice of many breeders of ducks and geese. They have co-operated in a splendid manner and, therefore, any virtues to be found in the book, will have been enhanced from their assistance.

With waterfowl the correct classification calls for "species" and "varieties". However, in the world of the fancier the more usual description employed is "breed". He or she speaks of breeds of ducks or breeds of geese to distinguish the various species. For this reason, wherever appropriate, the term "breed" has been employed and it is hoped that waterfowl enthusiasts will accept this usage as being appropriate.

Liss,   J. Batty.
Hampshire.

FRIENDLY: Joan Feeding her Geese
Despite what is sometimes thought geese can be quite friendly to their
owners.

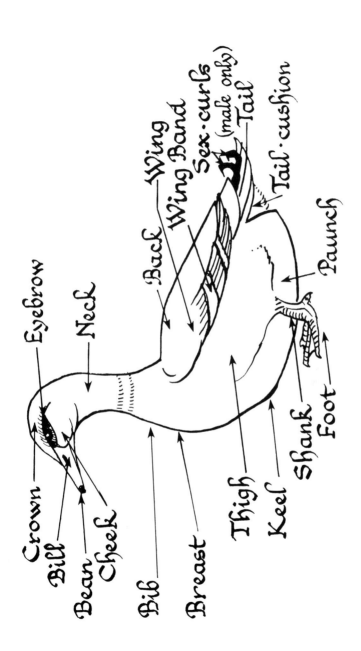

Figure 0.1 Points of the Duck

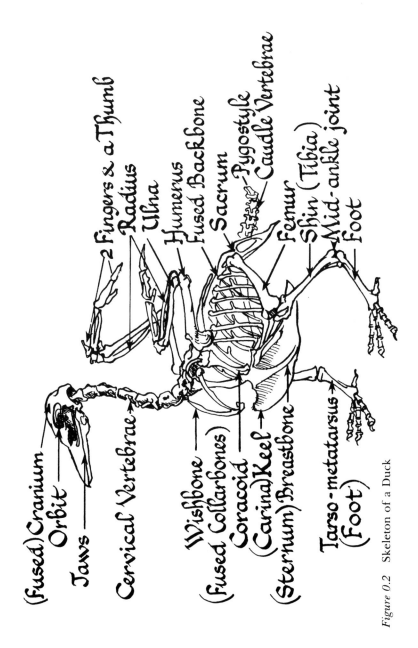

Figure 0.2 Skeleton of a Duck

White Italian Geese
First appeared in the Dairy Show of 1887, but is no longer seen in the
U.K.

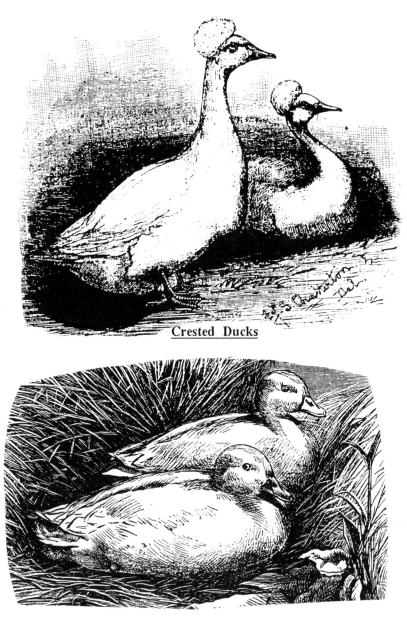

Crested Ducks

White Call or Decoy Ducks

Domesticated Ducks which are also "Ornamental".

Rouen Gander

A very striking bird about to take to the water

Sebastopol Goose with its Frills

Birds Which Impress as Being Unusual

TRUSTING: Ducklings with A Foster Father
The ducklings were abandoned by the hen which hatched them and
were fostered by a cock who brought them up.

Chapter 1

THE BREEDS

DUCKS

Domesticated ducks originate from wild waterfowl, from many countries, although most of the species appear to originate from Asia. (*Races of Domestic Poultry*, Brown, Edward). The progenitor is said to be *Anas boschas*, which is still seen as the Mallard. An exception is the Muscovy duck (*see* Chapter 12).

In its natural state the wild drake has one mate. The domestic drake has a number of wives – often six ducks will run with one male.

Many writers have commented on the relative drabness of the domesticated duck compared with the wild, but not all would agree. Each of the different varieties possesses its own charm combined, of course, with distinct utility properties.

Since ducks spend considerable time in the water they are built for that purpose. They are able to fly, dive and swim, and are more at home on the water than on land. The domesticated duck has adapted itself to a land existence and is able to live without swimming water, although, obviously, an adequate supply of drinking water is essential.

Over many generations domesticated ducks have been bred for specific purposes. They have been "improved" upon and *standards* have been established by the British Waterfowl Association and the Poultry Club. The main varieties are described later in this book.

GEESE

Geese are a type of waterfowl, and yet they are vegetarians, getting a considerable amount of their food from grazing. They do not originate from *one* common source, each variety having a different ancestor. For example, the Toulouse is descended from *Anser cinereus* (the Gey Lag goose). As a domesticated bird the goose has a long history; more than 4,000 years ago in Egypt it was regarded as a sacred bird. It provided flesh as food and feathers which have been used for various purposes; feather beds and quill pens being the most notable. Accordingly, it is essentially a bird of utility whose form has varied little from early times.

VARIETIES OF DUCK

The duck is very different from the domestic fowl. Its webbed feet allow it to swim, and to survive under the extreme conditions found on wet, muddy ground. Yet it can thrive just as well in a small enclosure *provided* its needs are present. The intake of food is via a serrated bill which allows the duck to lift food, or to suck through the serrations to obtain edible morsels. It will delight in poking into water holes or muddy pools to seek out titbits.

Ducks may be classified in a variety of ways; one possibility is as follows:

1. **Layers**
   (a) Khaki Campbell
   (b) Indian Runners
   (c) Orpingtons
   (d) Huttegem
   A White Campbell is also recognised but is rarely seen.

2. **Table or Utility Ducks**
   (a) Aylesbury
   (b) Blue Swedish
   (c) Crested
   (d) Pekin
   (e) Rouen (although not as acceptable as (a) or (d) because of its darker flesh).
   (f) Muscovy (again, not a first choice).

3. **Semi-Ornamental Ducks**
   (a) Call or Decoy Ducks
   (b) Cayuga Ducks
   (c) Black East Indian Ducks.

Not all fit neatly into a category. For example, Buff Orpingtons may lay 100-150 eggs per annum and yet are a good table duck.

For laying the Khaki Campbell is probably the most popular, whereas for table purposes the Aylesbury excels. However, sometimes ducks are crossed, thus attempting to achieve a compromise with satisfactory table and laying results. Whilst appreciating the reason for such crosses, the author-believes that the varieties are best kept in their pure state. Once crosses are made it becomes very difficult to trace ancestry. Moreover, developing a strain of pure bred ducks gives much greater satisfaction than a number of different colours, shapes and sizes. If both table and laying duck are required, keep a few of each – Aylesbury and Khaki Campbells.

Some of the minor breeds are not given above although many of these are included in the Chapter on *Other Varieties*.

VARIETIES OF GEESE

Not as many varieties of geese exist as for ducks. Nevertheless, the scope is tremendous and may provide a fascinating and profitable hobby for anyone with adequate pasture.

The main breeds are as follows:

1. Embden
2. Toulouse
3. Chinese
4. Roman Geese
5. Other varieties such as African and Sebastopol

Their usefulness as providers of food varies and, of course, much depends on the needs of the person keeping the geese. The Toulouse used to be one of the most popular geese, but their large frames certainly act as a deterrent to the average householder. Who fancies tackling a 30 lb goose for Sunday lunch! However, there is still scope at festive seasons, particularly Christmas, where the very large bird comes into its own.

Figure 1.1   Mallard Duck (*Anas boschas*) from which most species of duck orginate
(*Photo:* Vandyck Studios)

MANAGEMENT

Whether dealing with ducks or geese the essential requirements are similar:

1. **Healthy Stock** If showing is to be the aim then exhibition-type birds are absolutely essential. Generally speaking "farmyard" birds will reproduce the same type and it will take many generations to get them to show standards.
2. **Adequate Water** Running water or even a pond is not vital, but there should be adequate water for the birds to immerse their heads. A plentiful supply of fresh water is vital.
3. **Grass** Geese must have grass and ducks will certainly thrive better on grass although this is not essential for them. Runs should be rested, particularly when limited in size. Running stock on them should automatically manure the grass and improve its growth, but resowing with Ryegrass and White Clover may be essential when pasture is poor.
4. **Food and Grit** The food intake required will tend to vary according to the time of year and whether the stock are laying. If fed on pellets or a mixed mash ducks will take around 4 oz and geese around double that amount each day, but when grass and other natural food are plentiful the amount of food supplied can be reduced in quantity. Remember, though, these are approximate figures. *Ad lib* feeding on pellets may avoid underfeeding, but there is the disadvantage that the birds will take all they can

(Courtesy: Our Poultry, Harrison Weir)

Figure 1.2 Young Grey Wild Geese

eat and become lazy. However, this does not usually occur; the food in a hopper is generally taken to supplement the more attractive natural foods. Ducklings and goslings require special attention in the form of high protein foods.

5. **Housing** Housing of young stock is absolutely essential, especially in the very early stages. On the other hand, ducks and geese will thrive in any type of accommodation provided it is dry and fox proof.

These requirements are expanded in the chapters which follow. Ducks and geese are very hardy and besides providing a profitable pastime or "living" they can give immense pleasure to all who are interested in birds. Their active manner, the fascinating behaviour of the drake and duck of each breed, and the colourful display they provide, all contribute to the interest they provide.

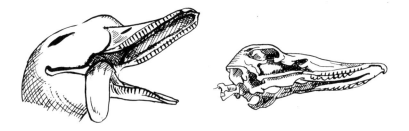

Figure 1.3   Duck's Head showing Serrated Bill

8

Chapter 2

THE RUN AND THE POND

SPACE REQUIRED

The amount of space required will be determined by the *objectives* of the person who wishes to keep the ducks or geese. If a few birds are to be kept, purely as a hobby, this will be quite different from where the main objective is to make money out of a commercial venture. If the latter is envisaged, a few acres of land will be essential.

For all purposes a pond will be a distinct advantage. This need not be large; indeed a small fibre-glass pond will suffice. This should be arranged in such a way that easy cleaning – emptying and refilling – is possible. Often running water from a hose-pipe until the pond overflows is sufficient, but periodically a complete clean out will be essential. Ideally though, some form of outlet will be essential for draining the pond.

When ducks are to be fattened too much exercise must be avoided. Furthermore, swimming should be *discouraged* and, therefore, a pond should *not* be provided. In such cases though, whilst with an appropriate diet larger weights will be achieved, there will be a tendency for fertility to suffer. This is not to say that breeding cannot be carried out. The author has seen many successful breeding programmes with no more than a good run and a relatively small water container such as an old sink or galvanized bath.

DOMESTIC DUCK KEEPING

When there is limited space a small number of ducks should be kept. All types of poultry can soon pollute a small area of land, but it can be specially so with ducks, who *wallow* in water and mud as a natural part of their daily lives.

Although, as noted earlier, running water is not essential, ducks will thrive better if there is a plentiful supply in which they can immerse their heads. If fertile eggs are required for breeding, a pond is very desirable. Indeed, some duck keepers state that a pond or lake is absolutely essential.

Like any "rule" there are exceptions. The author has kept Muscovy ducks in a grass run with water in a galvanized bath a metre in diameter with great success in breeding.

A garden, backyard, piece of woodland or orchard can serve equally well as a suitable run for ducks. The important points to remember are:

1. Do not overcrowd.
2. If possible, wire in an enclosure, permitting one part to be used whilst the other is rested.
3. Try to avoid the run being turned into a quagmire. This may be accomplished by one or more of the following:
   (a) Place a steel grill round the pond.
   (b) Lay flag stones at the edge of the pond.

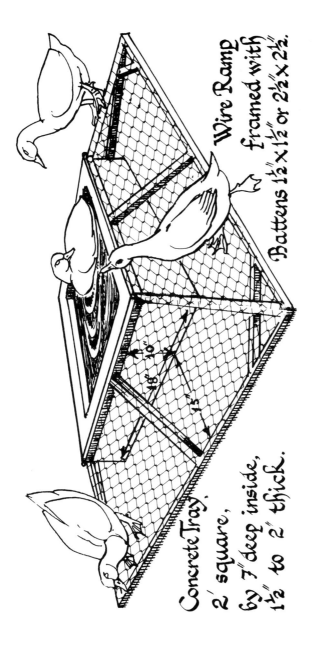

Wire Ramp framed with Battens 1½"×1½" or 2½"×2½".

Concrete Tray. 2' square, by 7" deep inside, 1½" to 2" thick.

18" 10"

13"

Figure 2.1   Wire Frame and Water Trough or Pond (keeps area around pond quite clean)

(Adapted from *Feathered World*)

(c) Put concrete around the pond with the "camber" allowing the water to run back into the pond.

(d) Have areas of gravel or small pebbles so that any dirt can be washed away with the rain or by the use of a hose.

These are all possibilities for making duck management easier for the duck keeper and represent an attempt to make life more tolerable for the ducks. However, it should be appreciated that ducks are foragers and making conditions too artificial can deprive the birds of much natural food and enjoyment.

An example of a small pond is given opposite. Housing should also receive attention, especially when predators such as foxes are around. This subject is covered in Chapter 3.

COMMERCIAL DUCK KEEPING

Even commercial duck keeping has different meanings, just as does commercial poultry keeping where a few egg producers have topped 1 million layers and others keep a few hundred. Accordingly, the set up will vary tremendously on the basis of land available, system of management, whether rearing for fattening or for laying and other considerations.

Various possibilities are as follows:

1. Grass run – usually not more than 100 ducks per acre is advocated to avoid problems such as mud, lack of grass or spread of disease.

2. Concrete floors of sheds and runs with frequent washing down to take away waste matter.
3. Large sheds with slatted floors on which the ducks move around. Below the slats there is a constant flow of water to take away all waste. This is the intensive system which keeps ducks inside, whether for laying or fattening.
4. Movable pens with one end placed in a stream. If foxes are around the underside of the pen must also be covered with wire netting.

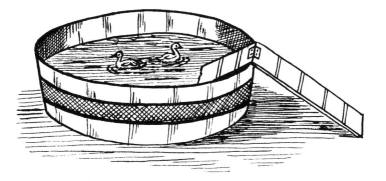

Figure 2.2   Small Surface Duck Pond

Some duck keepers advocate pens which hold around 25 ducks only and when the ground becomes soiled these are moved on until the grass grows again. Alternatively, a thick layer of pebbles or gravel forms the base and this is washed down. This is acceptable and helps to maximise the use of land, but it also deprives the ducks of grass which is very beneficial to them.

· Keeping a number of distinct pens as opposed to very large numbers of ducks in one pen does make management much easier. Moreover, smaller groups tend to give better results simply because they can feed better and performance can be assessed more accurately. One or two poor performers can be seen quite easily in a group of about twenty, but they are more difficult to spot when 100 or more are kept together.

Floor Covering

When concrete is used for the floor, some breeders advocate litter of some kind, especially in the sleeping area. Shavings, peat moss, leaves or even sand will provide covering to absorb moisture and make the ducks more comfortable. This should be cleaned out regularly and renewed.

If slats are employed they should be made of wood which is resistant to water. Alternatively, the slats may be impregnated with tar or other preservative.

Nest boxes may be provided with straw or other litter, thus enabling the ducks to lay in spots where eggs can be collected easily.

Food, Water and Grit

For commercial duck keeping it is essential to have correctly formulated foodstuffs according to the stage of develop-

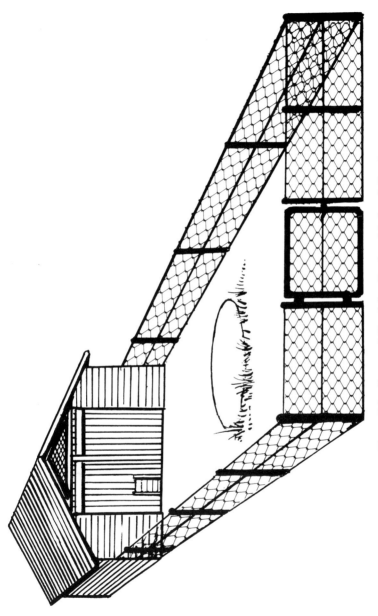

Figure 2.3   Run and Shed for Ducks with Small Pond

15

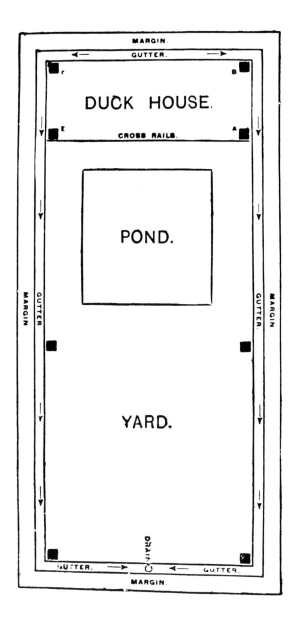

Fgure 2.4   Plan for construction of a Duck Yard

16

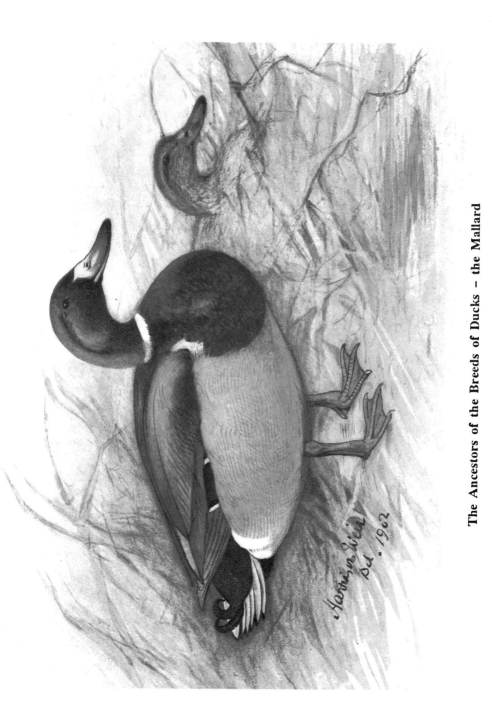

The Ancestors of the Breeds of Ducks – the Mallard

Top: Khaki Campbell Drake & Ducks
Bottom: Indian Runner Drake & Ducks (Fawn & White)

Top: Pekin Drake & Ducks
Bottom: Utility Type Rouen Drake & Ducks

Top: Blue Swedish Duck & Drake
Bottom: Cayuga Drake & Duck

Top: Crested Drake & Duck
Bottom: Orpington Duck & Drake
Note: The Buff colour varies and the above is on the dark side.

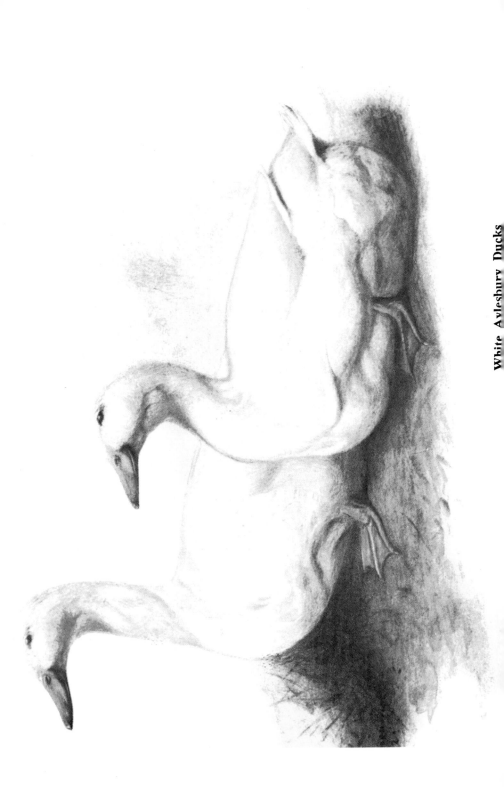

White Aylesbury Ducks

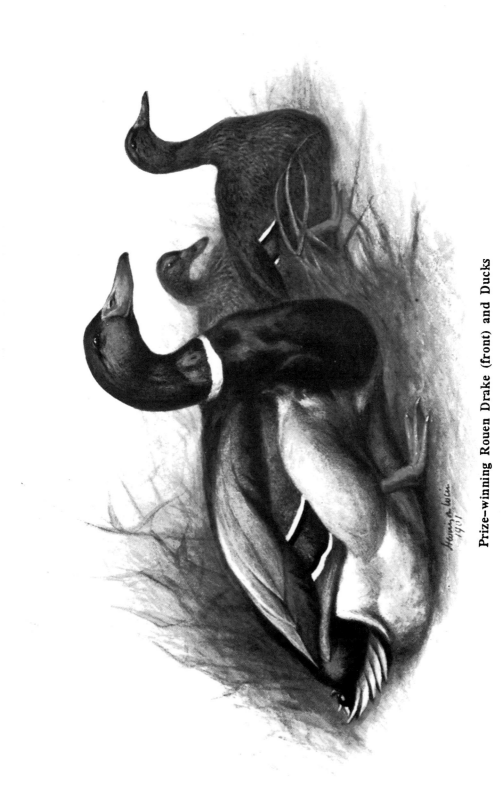

Prize–winning Rouen Drake (front) and Ducks

White Bibbed Black Drake & Duck

Possibly the black offspring of Blue Swedish, but known in Germany as "Duclair".

Figure 2.5 Water Fountain
Note: Obtain a fountain with a wide drinking area

Figure 2.6 Food Hopper

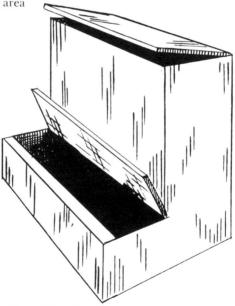

Figure 2.7 Grit Hopper
Note: Keep under cover or water will get into the hopper and make it rather 'sour'

ment or the purpose being achieved; thus:

1. **Starters** – usually turkey starter crumbs or chick crumbs.
2. **Growers** – turkey, broilers or poultry *growers'* pellets or mash.
3. **Layers** – layers' pellets or mash.

There should be a constant supply of fresh water. Long galvanized troughs with ball cocks and piped water can ensure that water is always present. This is vital and *regular checks* should be made to ensure that the water is always available. Remember, if ducks are deprived of water for just one day, quite serious consequences may result.

Along with food and water there should be a constant supply of oyster grit – this is particularly important when layers are being kept.

If a firm wishes to mix its own foodstuff it will be necessary to obtain the appropriate mixture of ingredients which gives the level of protein required. Mixing foods may save money, but it requires great skill and, of course, capital expenditure on storage facilities and grinding and mixing machinery.

PONDS

As noted earlier, swimming water is not vital for healthy ducks. They thrive and lay quite well without being able to swim. However, there are those who believe that better breeding results may be obtained with adequate swimming water.

Leaving any debate on one side, because there *are* differences of opinion on the necessity for a pond, what seems a certainty is that ducks benefit from being able to immerse

Figure 2.8   Fibre-glass Pond suitably landscaped

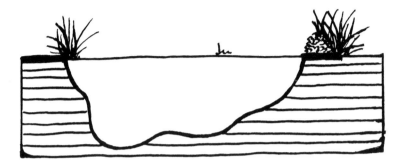

Figure 2.8 (cont.)   Cross section of fibre-glass Pond.

their heads in water.

Being able to control the amount of water can have considerable benefits which are listed below:

1. Laying or fattening ducks require a high level of food intake with adequate protein. Having a large pond with natural surroundings for foraging may result in ducks spending too much time away from nourishing food.

2. The water in a pond may become covered in green slime and, since ducks carry mud into a pond, unless drained regularly, may become silted up. It is always a source of great wonder how much mud can be "dumped" by a few ducks.

3. With a pond, *control* may be difficult. If let out too early ducks may lay on the water. At dusk there may be difficulty in enticing them off a pond to be closed in. Yet, if left, they may become wild and there is a serious danger of them being taken by predators, such as foxes.

These disadvantages have to be acknowledged. Yet birds must have some water or they will lose condition. Feathers become dry and, in extreme cases, mud and dirt will adhere to the feathers, causing considerable distress. The problem may be quite serious when there is no rain or when the birds are kept indoors. The author experienced a case recently where a pair of Aylesbury ducks were being kept by a farmer in a large intensive shed. The ducks were in a poor state of health (although well fed) and, upon being given a bath in a water tub and turned into a paddock, they quickly moulted and improved in condition. Water was provided in an old galvanized bath, but this was quite adequate to keep the birds fit.

Types of Pond
Ponds vary from the very small miniature receptacle to an enormous water-filled area such as a miniature lake – usually a natural pond. Most waterfowl fanciers will be content with a small pond which is economical to maintain.

If a natural pond is available this usually fills and drains itself and this is a considerable advantage. On the other hand, the small artificial pond will require regular cleaning out and refilling. Fortunately, with a hose pipe the cleaning process is fairly simple. If some form of plug and draining pipe is incorporated into the design, all the better.

Possible types of pond are as follows:

1. **Ready-formed Ponds**
These may vary from old sinks, galvanized baths or fibreglass ponds purchased from a pet or aquarium shop. Each of these is cheap, but care must be taken to camouflage sinks or other modified vessels. This is usually done by sinking the "pond" well into the ground and covering the

21

perimeter with flag-stones.

The preformed fibre-glass pond is a cheap and effective method of giving ducks a small area in which they can swim. A hole is excavated of the correct size and depth and the fibre-glass container is placed into it. At first the hole may not be exactly correct and, therefore, by trial and error the exact fit should be obtained.

2. Ponds made with Liners

A suitable sized area is excavated and then is made "leak proof" by lining with a suitable material. This may be one of the following:

    (a) **Polythene**
    (b) **P.V.C.** (poly-vinyl-chloride) suitably reinforced
    (c) **Butyl**

3. Concrete Ponds

A concrete pond, properly constructed, will probably outlast the other types. Obviously, though, it will take longer to make and may be more expensive.

There are a number of stages (after the hole is dug):

    (a) Build up a layer of concrete 3-4 inches thick using a stiff mixture.

    (b) Once the first layer is dried put on a further 3 inches, if necessary using battens to keep back the concrete to form the walls. Before dry, criss-cross the concrete.

    (c) *Finish off* with smooth concrete to which has been added a waterproofing agent.

The normal concrete should be made up of ballast (3 parts), sharp sand (2) and cement (1); whereas the final

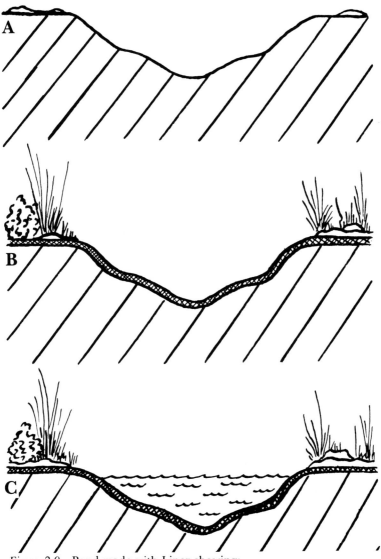

Figure 2.9 Pond made with Liner showing:
  A Excavation
  B Laying the polythene and securing the edges with earth, rocks and plants
  C Filling with water

mixture would be clean sharp sand (3) plus 1 part cement and, of course, the specified amount of waterproofing agent given in the manufacturer's instructions.

The final coat (the rendering) should be completed as quickly as possible to give a smooth finish and then allowed to dry slowly. In warm weather a covering of sacks or large paper bags might be advisable thus slowing down the drying process. Allow at least a complete week for the concrete to set and then fill with water and allow to stand for a period before allowing ducks to use the pond. However, there are some experts who suggest that the pond should be scrubbed and emptied and then refilled a few times before allowing any livestock to enter the water. Certainly fish and water creatures – so essential to make a pond interesting – would have difficulty in surviving with a high level of lime in the water (from the concrete). This is why changing the water a number of times is advisable.

Cultivating weeds or other plants around a pond makes the water area more attractive. If space is available a complete water garden can be made with a combination of small ponds, shrubs, garden ornaments and grass. This can look very attractive and adds to the beauty of any garden, with the ducks being a positive asset. The important point to watch is not to overstock or the water garden may become muddy and unsightly.

If reeds are to be planted it will be necessary to have "islands" of clayey soil at the edge of the pond into which the roots can be placed. Stones placed in appropriate positions will help to prevent the soil being washed to the bottom of the pond.

When a large natural pond is available a small island in the centre may be used as a refuge for the ducks against

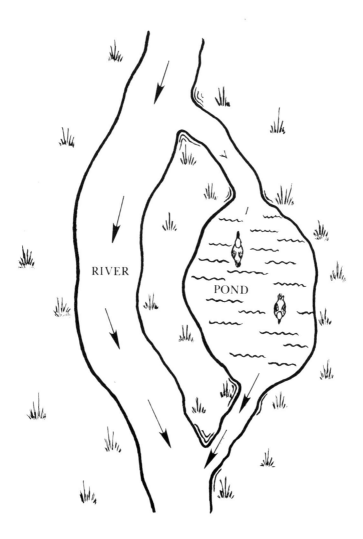

Figure 2.10 Pond made by using river

predators. Indeed, if left out on a night, this will be essential; otherwise the fox will quickly kill all the ducks. Remember though, that leaving ducks out will certainly reduce the yield of eggs because many will be laid on the pond or in places where they can be eaten by crows, magpies or jackdaws. To be sure all-round, ducks should be locked up each evening and let out around 8.30-9.00 a.m. when many of the eggs will then be laid.

WATER SUPPLY

An adequate water supply is vital. This may be supplied by a hosepipe augmented by rain – in appropriate circumstances rain water can be drained from the house roof and channelled into the pond. Where a pond is small and there are no means of draining, the hose should be allowed to run for a long period to allow the existing water to be cleared. Usually this means allowing the water to overflow for a period until the foul, stagnant water has cleared.

When a river is available this may be used to fill a pond and, through a suitable outlet, the water can be allowed to run back into the river. The positioning of the pond must be done with great care thus enabling the water to flow naturally round a loop which leads through the pond (*see* Figure 2.10).

If a river pond is possible, precautions will be necessary to make sure that the ducks do not stray on to the river and be carried away with the current or simply stray. A wire netting fence may be essential to avoid losses.

Chapter 3

ACCOMMODATION

BASIC PRINCIPLES

Ducks and geese are extremely hardy and, therefore, will make do with any type of shed. However, in designing or adapting a suitable shed the following requirements should be considered:

1. **Space per bird:**
   (a) Ducks – around 2 sq ft (0.186 sq metres) per duck;
   (b) Geese – around 3-4 sq ft (0.279-0.372 sq metres) per goose.
2. **Security from foxes and other predators**
   Foxes, rats, dogs, cats and other enemies may cause havoc in a shed which is not adequately protected. Concrete or wooden floors may be the answer to keep all the vermin out. However, from the point of view of cleaning out, when keeping ducks on a large scale, slatted or wire floors may be used.
3. **Ventilation and dryness**
   Ducks and geese will soon cause a very unhy-

gienic mess when kept in houses which are not adequately ventilated. There should be a regular flow of air through the shed and, in addition the floor should be kept quite dry. This may be done by using shavings, sawdust, peat moss, leaves or other litter and changed once it becomes soiled.

Straw or bracken can also be used, but it is best chopped up into short strands or it "holds" the moisture and very quickly becomes extremely boggy and messy.

TYPES OF HOUSE

There are so many types of possible houses or sheds that it becomes impossible to cover them all. Whether there is to be a large run also affects the size of house to be used. A small house may be feasible if there is a large run, (*see* Chapter 2).

In this chapter the housing of adult stock is considered. Chapter 4 deals with the housing for young stock.

HOUSING FOR DUCKS

Any type of gardening shed may be used for ducks and this gives head-room for going inside to collect the eggs. However, a lower shed will give greater economy in terms of wood.

Night house with ramp door

Figure 3.1 Small Duck House

This house is 8 feet by 4 feet and will hold around 12 ducks. The entrance for collecting the eggs is on the opposite side (not visible). Nest boxes may also be provided, but these are not vital.

Figure 3.2   Lean-to type of Duck House (opposite)

This lean-to shed is 6 feet by 4 feet with a height of 4 feet at the front and 3 feet at the rear.

Note carefully the ventilation section at the rear. At the front is the door, also with mesh at the top. The trap door pulls back.

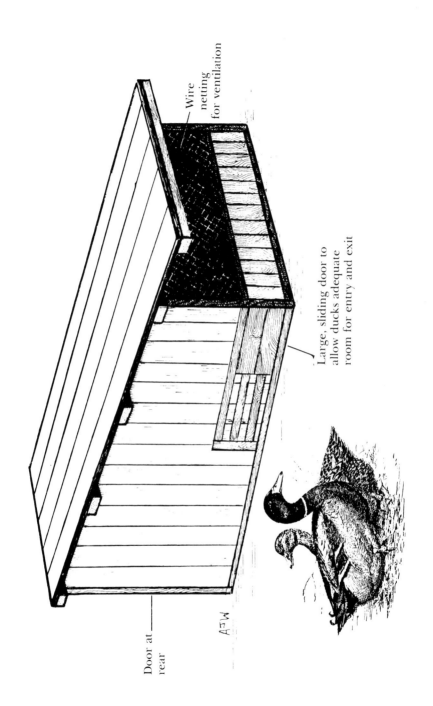

Wire netting for ventilation

Large, sliding door to allow ducks adequate room for entry and exit

Door at rear

31

Figure 3.3   Intensive-type Duck House (opposite)

With the intensive type of shed it is essential to allow for the following:

(a)   ventilation;
(b)   regular washing down;
(c)   a walk which is acceptable for the ducks – concrete or wire tends to be cold, wooden slats may be more acceptable.

In the structure shown the ducks are run in small groups and are kept quite intensively (divided by partitions). The floor slopes and is washed down regularly. The principle can be adapted to different sized houses, provided ventilation and other essentials are considered.

33

Figure 3.4   House for Geese

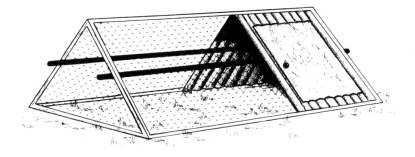

Figure 3.5   Fold Unit. Allows movement on the grass with carrying handles

34

HOUSES FOR GEESE

Any type of outhouse can be used for geese. On a farm the various outbuildings are ideal, provided they adjoin the field where the geese can graze.

Figure 3.4 House for Geese (opposite)

This house is constructed so that it can be moved around quite easily over the grass; note the handles at the end. A size of around 10 feet by 4 feet will give sufficient room for about 8 geese. The structure should not be made too large or it will be difficult to move without causing a strain on the frame. Where foxes are troublesome put wire netting across the floor (stapled to the bottom).

FATTENING DUCKS OR GEESE

When ducks or geese have to be fattened before selling or killing for table use, they may be confined for a period. This may be done in a shed similar to Figure 3.4 but with a section covered with wire-netting only. Alternatively, a fold unit may be used (*see* Figure 3.5).

In the case of geese the enclosure should be large enough for them to move around and stand upright. However, even so, this confinement should be limited to a few weeks. Geese thrive better if they have their full freedom. (*See* Chapter 19.)

Figure 4.1   Duck and Ducklings (From an old print)

Chapter 4

BREEDING

BREEDING DUCKS

Generally speaking, ducks are easier to breed than large fowl or bantams and are less trouble to rear. Ducks are hardy creatures and from about 10 days old, provided the weather is reasonable, they are able to fend for themselves. However, in winter or early spring when heavy frosts occur some form of heat may be necessary up to 28 days old. This will be the case at night when the temperature falls to around freezing point.

HATCHING

Hatching can take place at any time, the main limitation being the availability of eggs. Usually the best time is the spring when the ducklings will "grow into" the better weather. However, many duck breeders advocate the use of young ducks for early eggs in October when hatching can begin. This practice provides the spring ducklings which can be very profitable. Hatching can then continue to provide ducklings through to June.

These remarks apply to table ducklings and assume the

conventional pattern for demand – spring onwards. However, in modern times consumer habits have been subjected to sales propaganda and, with the widespread use of deep freezers, there is no longer the same need to produce and consume in the same period.

Many varieties of ducks do not come broody and therefore it will be necessary to use broody hens or an incubator (see later section on incubation). On the other hand, the Muscovy duck may be left to hatch her own eggs and some strains of Rouen are quite successful. The Aylesbury does not usually come broody.

For early hatched ducklings it will be necessary to use an incubator for the simple reason that broody hens are not generally available out of season.

Eggs should be collected daily and marked with the date. Around 12 eggs will be adequate for a setting. Settle the hen in a suitable box or coop on dummy eggs and after 1-2 days when she is sitting tight put the hatching eggs under her.

Take time and patience to settle the broody hens or many eggs will be lost. Remember a hen becomes attached to the nest in which she lays her eggs and in which she resolves to hatch them. A move to a different shed, where she can be in private, will most likely upset her so that she will not settle.

Try moving her after dark when she cannot see what is happening. Settle her down in the dark and then check the next day. If there is only one hen then confinement in a small shed in an open box will be fine. Leave water in a jar and mixed poultry corn in a container. The hen can then leave the nest at her own free will and return. If she does not leave, then after 48 hours remove her and let her run around and feed for around 10 minutes. Left too long some broodies will sit for excessively long periods and, without

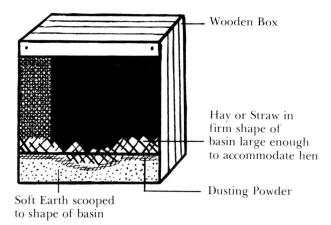

Wooden Box

Hay or Straw in
firm shape of
basin large enough
to accommodate hen

Dusting Powder

Soft Earth scooped
to shape of basin

Where two or more hens are housed
together, a door should be attached to
the front of the nesting boxes

Figure 4.2 Top   Typical Box for Broody Hen with details
     Bottom   Section with two Broody Boxes

39

food and water, may die.

Where two or more broodies are to be used then a coop with a door at the front should be used for each. In this way control can be exercised by letting out one at a time until they have been trained to return to their own nest. After 2 or 3 days a few at a time may be allowed to exercise. However, this method is very time consuming and unless care is taken a hen may finish up on the wrong nest. Sometimes two hens will insist on returning to the same nest with unfortunate results.

A free-for-all, where broodies are allowed to sit where they will, does not produce good hatching results. Preferably a broody should have privacy in a quiet place, where she can sit in peace and, when necessary, have exercise, food and water. Failure to provide the correct environment and attention will lead to indifferent hatches and disappointments.

The sitting box should be filled with damp soil, shaped into a large "basin" and lined with straw or hay.

SELECTION OF BREEDING STOCK

As a general rule stronger youngsters are bred from mature females – at least a year old, but preferably not more than 3 years old. Three ducks and a drake is the ideal combination and where a large run is available around 10 females and 3 drakes may be run together. However, do not run different varieties or breeds together or the results will be certain to include many "mongrels".

Where early hatched ducklings are desired then, as noted earlier, young stock birds may have to be used. Older birds will tend to be moulting in September, October or November whereas the young ducks hatched in the current year will commence to lay around September.

For good hatching results feed a layers' or breeders' ration. This may be obtained from the animal feeding mills in the form of mash or pellets; the latter are cleaner and there is less waste. Do not overfeed or the ducks will become too fat.

Ensure there is a plentiful supply of clean water which is kept "topped up". Although swimming water is not essential, the ducks should be able to submerge their heads in water. Access to grass or other green food is a positive advantage.

If exhibition birds are to be produced then top quality stock is essential. Establish the *standard* for the particular variety and then match the drake and ducks so that the "points of excellence" are brought out to the full on any progeny bred. The precise selection cannot be predetermined with certainty; this is why breeding winners is so difficult and yet so fascinating.

After keeping birds for some months visit breeders and the shows. Talk to those with experience of breeding and showing; if possible discuss the qualities of winners with judges and find out what was wrong with the losers. Do not expect to breed top quality birds easily. What is essential for long-term success is to breed good quality birds *consistently*.

BREEDING GEESE

Some breeds of geese such as the Embden will incubate their own eggs. However, when trying to manage geese on a commercial basis; obtaining the maximum number of eggs

41

from each goose, it will be advisable to "break off" the goose from her broodiness and get her into lay again as quickly as possible. This requires two essentials to be observed:

1. Collect eggs regularly, preferably twice each day.
2. Immediately there are any signs of a goose becoming broody and persisting, transfer her to a special coop for a few days and feed corn and a limited amount of water. Alternatively, use a fold unit to keep the goose off the nest. Keep the coop in the same run so that the remainder of the geese continue to see the "broody".

When a broody hen is to be used she should be placed in the coop described earlier, covering the appropriate number of goose eggs which will probably be around five, depending upon the size of the hen. Make sure she covers them correctly.

Some people believe in splashing water on the eggs each time the hen comes off, but this is not always necessary.

After the 30 days – possibly a day earlier – the young goslings should hatch. Leave the hen to her own devices, except to remove empty shells and, of course, any dead goslings. Hopefully the latter will not be present, but occasionally this does happen when the broody hen is careless or is "too keen" and squashes her brood.

BROODING

Geese may be reared by infra-red lamp, an oil lamp or a calor gas brooder. A small shed with the source of heat fitted is all that is necessary. The goslings can be allowed to run on grass after a few days, but should be watched very

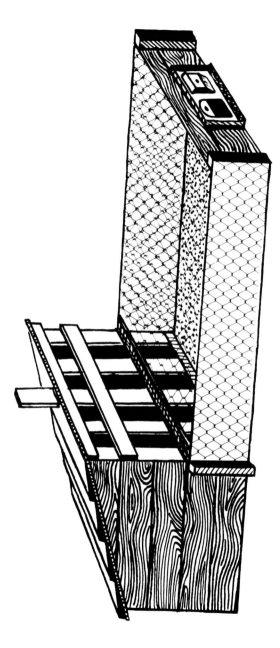

Figure 4.3 Coop and Run for Ducklings or Goslings

This type of coop and run is vital in the early stages. It can be moved regularly to fresh grass. Wire netting should be stapled underneath the run to avoid burrowing by foxes or rats.

43

carefully or crows, rats or other predators will take them. A covered run will be safer for a few weeks.

If reared by a broody hen, then a coop and enclosed run will be essential. This should be placed on grass and moved daily so that fresh grass is available. There should be a regular supply of water and, for the first few weeks, a regular supply of Turkey Starter Crumbs followed by other food.

In the early stages nourishing food is essential; grass alone will be inadequate for building up the goslings to the required size.

The water and food should be supplied from the second day and should be put in the run, under the protection of a door or board placed on top of the pen. Supply shavings in the bottom of the coop so that the hen and her brood are in dry surroundings and, of course, clean out and replace the shavings every few days.

Drowning a danger
Young ducklings and goslings, not allowed to go on to a pond for some time, may have difficulty in coping with swimming. Their plumage may not contain sufficient oils to avoid saturation and, therefore, they may have difficulty or even drown.

Introduce them to shallow water and watch for a few days to make sure that they are coping.

ARTIFICIAL INCUBATION

Hatching the eggs of ducks or geese by incubator can be very difficult. At one time the success rate was extremely low. In recent years, with the improvement in incubators

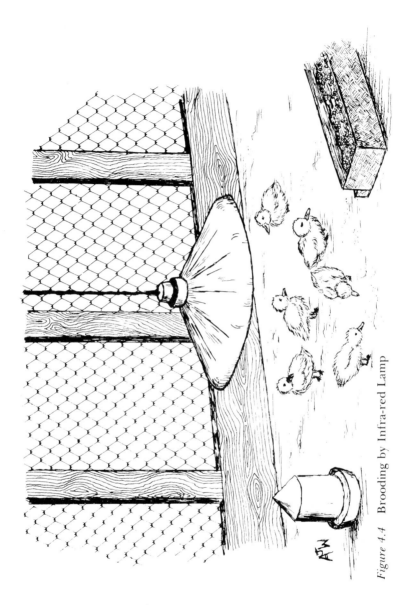

Figure 4.4 Brooding by Infra-red Lamp

Figure 4.5   Alternative Type of Field Rearer which may be moved around

and in techniques, very good results have been obtained, but for the amateur there is obviously a great deal of care and patience required.

The main requirements are:

1. Correct temperature without too much fluctuation.
2. Correct level of humidity – vital for any type of waterfowl eggs.

In all cases the instructions issued by the manufacturer of the incubator being used should be followed. Moreover, it should be appreciated that the incubation principles vary according to the type of machine being employed so *general* rules are difficult to formulate. For example, a machine which incorporates a fan for ventilation and diffusing the heat, is quite a different proposition from one which relies on the air rising by itself.

TYPES OF INCUBATOR

Broadly speaking incubators fall into two main categories:

1. **Still-air Incubators**
   These are usually small machines which hold from 25 to 300 hen eggs and obviously fewer duck or goose eggs. The heat is often over the eggs and there are ventilation holes at the bottom which allow the air to rise through the machine going through an outlet at the top.
   Moisture for humidity is usually provided in a container at the base of the machine and should be filled, say, once each week.
2. **Forced-draught Incubators**
   These incorporate a fan and heating elements

47

which bring the temperature to the appropriate level (usually around 99°F, 37.2°C). Both small and large machines incorporate this principle, although the fan does make a machine more expensive and for this reason is often provided in the larger machines only.

Turning
The smaller machines usually require turning to be done at least twice daily by hand. On the other hand, the large machines, having special loading trays into which the eggs are packed, allow eggs to be "turned" by moving the position of the trays. This may be done by the manual operation of a lever to move the trays or they may be turned quite automatically by electric motor.

Some of the more advanced smaller incubators incorporate automatic turning. Others use turning rings which allow the eggs to be turned by a simple movement of the rings.

Important statistics
Temperature, humidity and ventilation are all closely related. Fortunately, provided manufacturer's instructions are followed, an acceptable level of hatching should result. Vital statistics for incubation and rearing are as follows:

INCUBATION

Week	Ducks temp	Geese temp	Ducks and Geese Humidity
1	99.2°F (37.3°C)	99.0°F (37.2°C)	Dry Bulb
2	99.2°F (37.3°C)	99.0°F (37.2°C)	99.8°F (37.7°C)
3	99.0°F (37.2°C)	98.5°F (36.9°C)	Wet Bulb
4	—	98.5°F (36.9°C)	87.9°F (31°C)

48

The temperature reading will depend on the type of machine. When a *separate* hatcher is used the eggs are transferred 3 days before hatching and the humidity is increased for the last 2 days. However, each machine is different so the precise instructions must depend on the maker's handbook.

REARING

Ducks and geese

Week	°F	°C
1	95	35
2	86	30
3	77	25

All writers on waterfowl hatching emphasize the need for a high level of humidity. However, if still-air machines are opened too frequently there is a danger of over-evaporation of eggs*, even with a very high humidity.

In connection with rearing ducklings and goslings it should be noted that in the late spring and in the summer the sooner they are taken off heat, the better they will be. Indeed, quite often a compartment lined with hay will give sufficient heat after the first week or two, so no artificial heat is necessary. Remember, though, that if there is any danger from frost some form of heat will be essential to keep the young stock warm during the night.

SEXING DUCKS AND GEESE

The drawing opposite shows how to sex young ducklings. If the cloaca is stretched the penis of the male duckling can be seen. Any sexing should be done in a warm room and if in doubt use a magnifying glass.

*For interesting notes on this problem see "Hatching Waterfowl Eggs" by Alex Fairhurst, *BWA Bulletin*, 1975.

Sexing goslings may be done in a similar way, but is more difficult. At baby stage the penis is around ½ inch long. The process needs more experience, but the safest method is at 7 months of age or older when the gander's penis may be seen. The bird should be placed on its back and the genital organs examined.

When geese are mature they may be distinguished by physical characteristics such as:

1. larger knob for gander in Chinese geese;
2. larger size in gander; at 2 months old the neck and head will be thicker than in the goose;
3. aggressiveness – gander tends to be more aggressive, protecting the geese and "hissing";
4. a more pronounced, double pouch in the goose.

Older *ducklings* (around 2 months of age) may be sexed by the sound of the quack which in the duck is quite clear and in the drake has a deeper sound, sometimes described as a "croak". As the voice develops the test becomes more foolproof, but a fancier needs practice before being absolutely certain.

As ducks and geese grow older and the plumage appears, where there is different plumage for a drake or gander, this will be a sign, but for self coloured ducks this is no guide. Often the main indication is when the curled feather of the male appears, but even this is not infallible.

COLLECTING AND STORING EGGS

The eggs are the foundation for successful hatching. Neglected eggs inevitably lead to poor hatches. Rules to follow

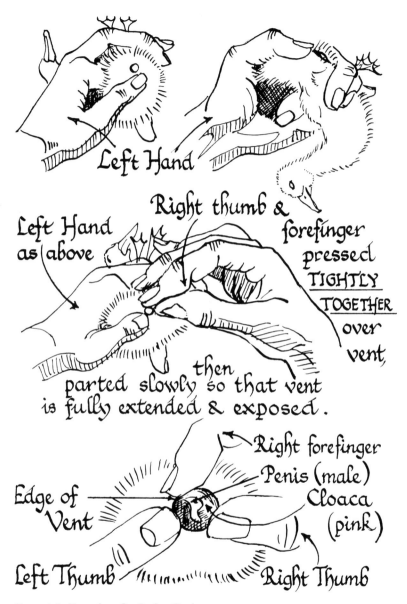

Left Hand

Left Hand as above

Right thumb & forefinger pressed TIGHTLY TOGETHER over vent,

then parted slowly so that vent is fully extended & exposed.

Right forefinger
Penis (male)
Cloaca (pink)

Edge of Vent

Left Thumb
Right Thumb

Figure 4.6 Procedure for Sexing Ducks
(From the *British Duck Keepers Association Year Book*)

51

are as follows:

1. Collect eggs early in the morning and clean off any mud. Some writers state that eggs should not be washed, but it has been shown that the hatch improves when a mild disinfectant is used to sterilize eggs. This implies that eggs must be washed in some way.
2. Keep eggs for not longer than 7 days in a cool temperature (10-15°C, 50-59°F).
3. When the eggs are set, put the date on the small end of the egg or, in large incubators, put the date on a label in the tray.
4. Turn eggs regularly both when being stored and in the incubator. At least twice a day is essential.

Chapter 5

AYLESBURY DUCKS

BRITISH SUPREMO

Undoubtedly, the Aylesbury duck is the principal table bird. It achieves around 8-10 lb and the white skin makes the bird a very attractive meat proposition. Sometimes a cross is made with the Pekin which is a favourite in the U.S.A. This may increase size and vigour although whether this practice can be justified is debatable. The Pekin has a yellow skin and is not regarded as having the same superior flavour as the Aylesbury.

This variety originated in the Vale of Aylesbury in Buckinghamshire. Many years ago the duckling industry was well established in that area. It was believed that the Aylesbury could be reared within the clearly defined regional area and nowhere else. Without doubt, the specialisation which developed in the area contributed to the success achieved in the production of table ducklings. However, Aylesbury ducks are now reared and managed in all parts of the U.K., the U.S.A., and many other countries.

MAIN FEATURES

The Aylesbury is a pure white duck which grows rapidly and reaches a considerable size (around 10 lb). A deep, broad body is a characteristic, with the keel almost touching the ground. The wings are carried high around the body. A prominent breast is essential; so is a horizontal carriage.

The wedge-shaped bill (set in a strong head), should be white or flesh pink. Any tendency towards yellowness may be an indication of loss of the white skin – an undesirable feature when top table birds are required.

Figure 5.1   Exhibition-Type Aylesbury

Fortunately, exhibition and utility *standards* are very much in harmonty. These are indicated in Figure 5.1, the Aylesbury drake. However, utility birds often lack the very deep keel.

The **deep keel** is an essential feature in exhibition birds. Over the years the very low body has been developed to an exaggerated state. Many think that the process may have gone too far. However, those who breed exhibition birds will know that only a small minority reach top class and, therefore, the majority of Aylesbury ducks will be fit only for the table. If the interest is in utility birds then the exaggerated keel is best avoided, but still aim for typical birds – those which fatten quickly.

EXHIBITION TYPES

For exhibition a *massive* bird should be the aim with the following features:

1. Body should be long.
2. Breast should be prominent – many leading specimens have an almost straight breast from the base of the keel to the neck.
3. Keel should follow a straight line without excessive "looseness" or "bagginess" at the rear. Much depends upon the sex and age of the bird, but, generally speaking, too much bagginess is a sign of internal fat in the wrong place.
4. Bill should be long and coming straight out "like a woodcock's" (Lewis Wright). Care must be taken to keep the bill pink and thus may involve keeping exhibition ducks away from muddy conditions; too much sun should be avoided and, when necessary,

any yellow scale should be removed very carefully and sandpapered to a smooth finish. However, there should be no question of "faking" or a bird could be disqualified.

5. Legs should be in the middle of the long body and this requirement is essential for the *horizontal carriage* without which the *type* is not present. The colour of the legs is bright orange.

6. Body colour is white and, obviously, for exhibition purposes a thorough wash in warm water and a mild detergent is recommended – followed by a double rinse. A few days should be allowed for complete drying.

Figure 5.2   Pen of Utility Aylesbury Ducks

Figure 5.3 **Top**: Typical Shape of Aylesbury
Bottom: Show Pens with Aylesburys (Must be used
for training for shows)

The older writers recommended keeping exhibition birds in a covered run with a pan of water and sharp white gravel to which is added wheat to encourage the ducks to forage. This has the effect of keeping the bill clean and white.

GETTING THE SIZE

Once colour and type are established the aim should be to obtain *size*. Suitable accommodation and an appropriate run are essential (*see* Chapters 2 and 3). Above all, a high protein food is necessary to develop the massive body. Corn put into a water trough is a typical diet, but for exhibition stock (and for fattening birds), it will not produce the maximum results. A layer's mash (or pellets) is much better (discussed in a later chapter) and this may be left before the birds at all times in a suitable hopper.

Special fattening foods may also be employed. In the early stages Turkey Starter Crumbs may be used. These would be followed on with high protein foods which may be ready made from the local mill or may be mixed at home (*see* Chapter 17). Remember the aim is to have the birds ready for killing within 7 to 9 weeks of age.

LAYING QUALITIES

The Aylesbury duck lays a large egg (around $3\frac{1}{4}$ oz, 92 g) which is white or greenish white. Numbers laid in a year vary, but as many as 100 per year is quite common and an annual output approaching 200 is possible – no mean achievement for a "meat" bird. However, since meat production and high-yield egg laying are opposing aims, most breeders are content to obtain around 80-100 eggs.

BREEDING

For *exhibition purposes* two or three ducks to a drake is the usual recommendation. Select birds which have a large frame, but are neither too old nor too fat. All birds should be of the appropriate type with the desired deep keel. Do not expect to breed top class birds from small parents quite untypical of the true Aylesbury. If just starting, be careful when purchasing stock. Many advertisements specify "Aylesbury-type birds" which may simply mean large white ducks. Therefore, do make sure by enquiring from the breeder or, better still, pay him a visit. For a pair of top quality birds expect to pay a considerable sum.

On the other hand, if not interested in showing, the Aylesbury duck which is not "keeley" may be quite adequate. It will fatten quickly and grow to the necessary 5 lb or more within 9 weeks. Moreover, the breeding pen may consist of around six ducks instead of the three recommended for exhibition stock.

For the best breeding results feed a layer's ration and provide the ducks with an adequate run. Any type of run will suffice, but ideally this should be in a small paddock, grass covered. Alternatively, a small orchard or an enclosed part of the garden will suffice, but remember, an area may become "sour", especially when drainage is poor. This is the advantage of the well-drained grass run.

An alternative to grass or earth for the floor of the run is fine gravel. The whole of the area should be dug out and filled with stones, rubble, pebbles and fine gravel in that order. In addition, there should be a frame with a grill-type cover, adjoining or surrounding a small pond (*see* Chapter 2), thus allowing adequate drainage.

The general strategy with a gravel surface is to allow the rain to wash down the surface which can be supplemented with a thorough spraying down with a hose pipe.

This approach may be acceptable for very small ducks, but the larger ducks such as Aylesburys require considerable space. Exercise and a foraging area are essential for healthy ducks.

Chapter 6

BLACK EAST INDIAN DUCKS

Because of its smallness (around 2 lb) many regard the Black East Indian duck as a Bantam duck. The precise origin is obscure; it is thought to originate in South America and is possibly developed directly from the Mallard (as a sport).

This variety could be regarded as a semi-ornamental. The colour is beetle-green with tremendous sheen, thus making them very attractive birds.

It is not in the top class as a commercial duck either for laying or table. However, it is a moderate layer and there are those who believe that its flesh makes the Black East Indian a worthwhile table bird – despite its smallness.

According to J.T. Brown (*Encyclopaedia of Poultry*, o.o.p) the great Darwin referred to these ducks as "Labrador", and noted that they breed true. Other names used are "Buenos Airean" and Brazilian.

MAIN CHARACTERISTICS

The colour of the Black East Indian duck is magnificently striking with its beetle-green sheen and black legs and webs.

It has a short, compact body clear of the ground. The neck is short and the head round-shaped with a black bill.

The general appearance is that of the Mallard with a horizontal carriage.

EXHIBITION REQUIREMENTS

A neat, graceful bird is required with ideal colouring. Accordingly, major faults are as follows:

1. Coarseness and oversize.
2. Whiteness in plumage.
3. Purple or brown colouring.
4. Wrong colour bill or legs; i.e., other than black.
5. Little or no green sheen.
6. Upright carriage.
7. Deformities or uncharacteristic features such as dished bill.

For breeding exhibition stock it is advisable to breed only from correctly coloured birds of the appropriate size.

When conditioning ducks for a show special attention should be paid to feeding in a manner which brings out the colour. Many believe that extra greenstuff is beneficial and there is no doubt that consistent feeding of a good quality poultry feed is essential. The use of cod liver oil and linseed jelly is also advocated by many breeders.

Special points

The *standards* stipulate colour, shape, size and other requirements. However, the interpretation is of the utmost importance. Special points to watch are as follows:

1. Colour

Expect the drake to be a greener, more vivid colour than the duck. Getting the absolutely black/green colour on ducks is very difficult; often there is an underly-

Figure 6.1　Black East Indian Ducks
(From *Our Poultry*, Harrison Weir)

ing dark brown colour. If too obvious then the duck should be penalised, but only a tinge of very dark brown with black predominating should not call for disqualification. Obviously, though, the *aim* should be to achieve as black a bird as possible.

2. Bill

The *standard* for the *drake* calls for a *black* bill and this is the ideal. However, according to that great authority Lewis Wright (*Illustrated Book of Poultry*) the true colour is "a sort of pale yellow washed over with blackish green, the colour being laid on *thinly*, as it were, to give an almost transparent effect, and shaded off at the tip into a kind of slate-colour".

Even when the black bill is achieved, with age this becomes lighter. At 2 years of age there will be difficulty in maintaining the deep black colour.

With *ducks* the darker, black bill may be achieved more frequently. Green patches on the bill should be penalised.

3. White Feathers

The existence of white feathers is a fault. Yet many good specimens do get a few of these, especially round the eyelids and at the base of the lower mandible. As birds grow older they may grow more white feathers.

4. Size and Shape

For exhibition purposes small, stylish birds are required. They should have short bodies and round heads, with neat, short bills

BREEDING WINNERS

Black East Indian ducks are not difficult to breed, but exhibition stock *must* be bred from birds true to *type*. Over-

Figure 6.2   Black East Indian Duck showing standard type
     Top: Illustration showing shape to comply with standard
 Bottom: Bird with many faults. Do not breed from this type

65

sized stock will tend to produce larger, coarse birds which are of little value for showing. This applies to the breeding of all exhibition stock, but when small, elegant birds are required the mixing of blood tends to increase size.

UTILITY PROPERTIES

These ducks fatten quite well and require no special management or feeding. In appropriate conditions they will fend for themselves, feeding on insects, slugs and other titbits. However, for the best results it is better to give them some food, but do not overfeed.

Black East Indian ducks can fly extremely well, but will settle quickly and, therefore, any flying around will be done within a reasonable area. However, at times it will be advisable to clip the feathers of *one* wing; e.g. when space is limited or when introducing birds to new surroundings.

They lay a reasonable number of eggs and are plump. Because of the small, light bone there is not much waste. Obviously, they cannot hope to compete with Aylesbury or Rouen duck for quantity of meat, but the *quality* is present.

HATCHING

The eggs may be hatched by large fowl, bantams or ducks, or artificially by using an incubator. Provided not more than two or three ducks are run with a drake fertility should be good.

Ducklings when hatched are very dark in colour (blackish) with a shade of yellow on the breast. At first they will appear frail, but after a few days grow quickly. Instructions for rearing ducks are given in Chapter 4.

Chapter 7

CALL DUCKS

The Call duck comes into a similar category to the Black East Indian duck. It is in a mid-way category between the "commercial" and the ornamental.

They develop into plump ducks which, when killed and plucked, make excellent table birds – although small (under 2 lb) – yet the general attractiveness endears them to the exhibition or waterfowl enthusiast.

In shape the Call is what fanciers call "cobby" – round, compact, firm and yet plump. The neck is short and the bill is small, set low on a rounded forehead.

Another description is the "Decoy" duck, so called because it is employed to attract wild birds for shooting or trapping. The constant *quacking* – the "call" – brings in the Mallard who, unsuspecting, fly in to join other ducks who are feeding. This has been summed up as follows:

> "Exceedingly good sport may be obtained, especially on a very stormy day, by placing a few decoy ducks within good range of a gun stationed near the bank of a sheltered bay or eddy. The decoy can also be used with success when ducks are flighting to crop or roots."
>
> *The Keeper's Book*, Sir Peter Jeffrey Mackie, Bart.

EXHIBITION REQUIREMENTS

When judging Call ducks it is necessary to look for *type*.

Figure 7.1   Wild Duck decoying   (From an old print)

Accordingly, attention should be paid to the main features, establishing *to what extent* actual and standard requirements agree. More specifically the following should be examined:

1. **Size**
   Should be a small cobby bird; therefore, any feature which departs from the *norm* should be penalised; for example:
   (a) slim bodied;
   (b) tall;
   (c) wings long and loose;
   (d) lack of full breast;
   (e) carriage not horizontal;
   (f) long back.

2. **Head and Neck**
   The head is required to be round in shape and set on an extremely short neck. Accordingly, a long neck or a small head would be unacceptable. A bill which is narrow or long would also constitute a major defect.

3. **Colour**
   Various colours have been developed, the most usual being the "wild" duck colour (like the Mallard). There is also a white and some "off colours" such as Blue, Buff, and Black and White.
   Any departure from the wild duck colour, such as no white neck ring or absence of deep claret colour in breast (in the drake), should be penalised. With the self colours there should be no other colour, other than White, Blue or Buff as the case may be.
   Call ducks are best kept on a grass run which allows them plenty of exercise. If confined too

much, care must be taken not to overfeed or they may grow too large, thus exceeding the maximum weight.

Figure 7.2   Grey Call Ducks
(From *The Poultry Book*, W.B. Tegetmeier)

Chapter 8

CAMPBELLS

ORIGINS

The original Campbells – White and Khaki – were created by a Mrs. Campbell of Uley, Gloucester. According to a reputable source*, an Indian Runner duck, an excellent layer, was mated to a Rouen drake. This was followed by the introduction of the Wild duck (Mallard) and the progeny became the basis of the breed known today.

In fact, the *original* Campbell, introduced to the public in 1898 was a darker bird than the Khaki which was finally developed. In its original form the characteristics were as follows:

Drakes: Dark green heads and bills, grey backs, pale claret breasts, legs yellow, sterns black, slight ring around neck and weight around 5 lb.

Ducks: Feathers greyish-brown pencilled with dark brown, plain brown head, no streak from eye, dark bill, and yellow legs (weight 5 lb).

This creation laid around 200 eggs per annum, but there were many who wanted birds which were more pleasing in

Encyclopaedia of Poultry, J.T. Brown (out of print).

appearance. Therefore, the buff colour of the Khaki was strengthened without losing the laying capabilities. Within a few years the present-day *standard* was established with the emphasis on an overall Khaki colour (see below).

From the Khaki there emerged the White Campbell described as a "sport". The colour should be pure white with the legs, webs, and bill a vivid orange.

The Dark Campbell is different from the original "dark" as introduced by Mrs. Campbell. The creator was a Mr. H.R.S. Humphrey of Devon and he was seeking a species which would provide sex linkage, (see *British Poultry Standards*). The principal difference in colour is that the main colour is a light brown, (instead of buff).

Like many new creations, the White and Dark never became popular. When reference is made to the Campbell as a laying duck it is the Khaki Campbell which is meant.

MAIN REQUIREMENTS

The original creator of the Campbell was seeking to establish a general purpose type of duck which would lay extremely well and yet have a reasonably sized carcass for roasting. She succeeded in developing birds which may lay well over 300 eggs in a year and yet reach a weight of 5 to $5\frac{1}{2}$ lb for drakes and $\frac{1}{2}$ lb lighter for ducks.

Looked at sideways the Campbell should have a gently sloping carriage from the tip of the tail up to the head which is carried quite high (an angle of around 35 degrees). There should be no question of an upright position like the Indian Runner nor a low keel like the Aylesbury or Rouen. Obviously the result is a compromise which shows a duck which is agile and sprightly.

Since the aim is to have ducks which are energetic —

72

constantly seeking food which is converted into eggs – any sign of sluggishness or coarseness should be deprecated.

The plumage for both duck and drake should be close fitting; in the language of the poultry fancy a bird with close fitting feathers is known as "hard feathered". However, it will be appreciated that no ducks are really *soft* feathered so the marked differences found with different breeds of fowl are not present with ducks.

Campbells are *layers* and any characteristic which is alien to this essential requirement should be looked upon with disfavour.

Figure 8.1   Khaki Campbell Drake

EXHIBITION REQUIREMENTS

The essential requirements for Campbells are as indicated earlier. For the *detailed* description of each colour reference should be made to *British Poultry Standards*. Since the main colour is the Khaki Campbell references are to that variety.

In summary form the requirements are as follows:

1. Head and neck of *drake* should be dark bronze with a green sheen. The tail should be a similar colour.
2. With the duck the head and neck should be medium brown.
3. Both duck and drake should be an even shade of khaki colour.
4. Legs and webs should be deep orange in the male and a "khaki" colour in the female.
5. The bill should be a dark colour, described as greenish blue (drake), or greenish black (duck). However, some latitude is allowed, but a light coloured bill (e.g. yellow) should be penalised (a serious defect).
6. Type: birds should not be too heavy or coarse. Campbells are essentially slim, active ducks.
7. Other faults mentioned in the *standards* are as follows:
   (a) White in the form of odd feathers in the plumage or white neck rings.
   (b) Streaks from eyes in ducks.
   (c) Deformities.

Figure 8.2 An interesting (historical) illustration of KCs with white necks and undercarriage – no longer seen and not recognized, but quite attractive.

Getting ready for the show

For achieving top show condition it is essential to keep the stock in conditions which allow plenty of exercise and plenty of greenstuff. A small paddock or orchard is ideal. There should be plenty of shade to keep the direct rays of the sun from fading the colours.

The aim should be to produce:

(a) a dark bill (greenstuff does this);
(b) sound colouring in legs;
(c) correct stance of 35 degrees;
(d) even coloured khaki topped by a dark bronze head in the drake (not too much green), and by a medium brown head in the duck.

The aim is to produce fit, healthy ducks. For show purposes select good coloured specimens. Avoid too much green in the drake which is a legacy from the Mallard; it leads to producing females which are also like the Mallard.

A healthy drake can cope with around 6 ducks. Reasonable exercise, food with a high protein level, and an adequate water supply, should supply all the essential needs for fertile eggs.

Mrs Campbell

Chapter 9

CAYUGA

The Cayuga (or **Black Cayuga**) originates from the U.S.A.
and is said to take its name from Lake Cayuga. In colour it is
Black throughout with a brilliant green sheen. The bill
should be dark (The British *Standard* specifies slate-black),
and the legs and webs should be an orange-brown (*not*
bright).

Comparisons are sometimes made with the Aylesbury
and in weight the male Cayuga, at around 8 lb, is quite near
to the Aylesbury. However, it never *looks* as large, not having the deep massive body of the British duck. In addition,
the carriage is not as horizontal as the Aylesbury.

There is great similarity to the Black East Indian duck
described earlier. Some breeders believe that the Cayuga is
really an oversized Black East Indian. However, this conjec-
ture does not lead anywhere; the Cayuga is a *distinct* variety.

Its attractiveness means the Cayuga could count as an
ornamental duck. Yet the ducks lay quite well and are also
suitable as table birds. Many consider Cayugas are very
underrated. Undoubtedly they are, but in Britain the yellow
skin is disliked by some people. This may be more illusory
than is justified by facts; the white flesh is firm and is of a

good flavour.

A more serious problem are the black stubs left after plucking. These disfigure the carcass and their removal goes against the Cayuga as a commercial possibility. On the other hand, the small breeder, looking for a duck which may be used for exhibiting as well as having utility properties, could well be satisfied. The colour is not as difficult to maintain for showing as the pure white ducks which very quickly look yellow or "boiled".

Figure 9.1   Black Cayuga Drake

Figure 9.2   Pair of Black Cayugas
(*Courtesy:* Charles and Maggie Piper, Alford Acre)

EXHIBITION REQUIREMENTS

In the British *Standard*, type is given 30 points; this covers the long broad body with its prominent breast. The neck is long with a large, prominent head.

Surprisingly, only 15 points are awarded to colour. Yet a Cayuga of the *wrong* colour can hardly be given top awards. Serious defects are white or red features and "objectionable" is a purple or brown tinge. Lacing is also a defect. In other words, departure from the green-black plumage should be avoided.

Figure 9.3   Cayuga Duck showing standard type

Top: Typical size and shape
Bottom: Poor specimen

Feeding may have an important effect upon the colour achieved. The full green sheen is obtained by giving birds a plentiful supply of greenstuff. If they can be run on a grass run which is well drained, no difficulty should be experienced in maintaining condition. An excessive amount of poultry corn may cause deterioration in plumage. If the ducks are given access to layers' crumbs it will be found that condition is kept for a longer period.

Defects
From what has been stated it will be apparent that possible *defects* are as follows:

1. **Colour** – other than black with green sheen.
2. **Size** – avoid small, underweight birds. However, a medium sized bird in excellent condition may beat a large, dull bird which is clearly out of condition.
3. **Shape** – birds lacking the full breast and having shallow bodies do not conform to *type*. A very narrow back is also a fault.
4. **Strong head and neck** – birds with small heads and weak necks do not present the strong, virile duck expected of the Cayuga.
5. **Legs** – any departure from the midway positioning of the legs would be a penalty. This would affect the carriage; if too upright this would indicate a cross with the Indian Runner or Pekin. Yet a perfectly horizontal carriage is not expected or desirable.

CONCLUSION

The Cayuga is an attractive duck which, in good condition, can present a very attractive picture. As a forager it takes some beating and is very hardy. For the exhibitor who likes a black duck this is probably the best – as a practical proposition which lays at an acceptable rate and can be used for the table.

Cayuga Ducks

Chapter 10

CRESTED DUCKS

ORIGINS

The crest of the Crested duck is set towards the back of the head, and the larger the size of the crest the better. Another requirement is a **round** crest set in the centre of the head. Obviously because the duck is described as a **Crested** more attention is paid to this aspect than any other, although the *standard* gives a weight of 25 points only. Naturally a "well-balanced" duck is necessary, but a weak crest will disqualify.

Where the Crested originated is uncertain. The Poultry Club *Standard* states that this is a British duck, but some writers have suggested that Holland is probably the country of origin. The existence of Crested ducks in old Dutch paintings is used as evidence of this fact. That famous authority Harrison Weir uses this source in his book *Our Poultry*.

The same author refers to them as the "Top-Knotted" ducks. He believed they were a freak of nature in the first instance. They were then bred from, and improved upon, so that large round crests became possible. An example of one of these birds is given overleaf.

83

Another authority, Lewis Wright, states that the variety is said to originate in the East. However, he was of the opinion that the Crested duck was a sport from the common duck.

Figure 10.1 Crested Duck   (*Photo courtesy:* Anita-Dawn Allen)

Figure 10.2 Group of Crested Ducks
(*Photo courtesy:* Anita-Dawn Allen)

MAIN CHARACTERISTICS

The Crested is a medium sized duck (around 6-7 lb). In attempting to describe the *type* the British *Standard* states that the Crested is rather like the Orpington. An early breeder, Mr. Scott Miller, thought the variety was rather like an undersized Aylesbury (quoted by Lewis Wright).

Quite naturally for many people the crest brings the duck into the ornamental category. This is quite wrong; they are utility birds which lay reasonably well and also put on weight very well.

85

Figure 10.3   Crested Duck showing standard type
  Top: Bird showing required type of crest
  Bottom: Duck exhibiting weak crest and examples of faulty
             crests

If the crest is to be perpetuated and improved upon, it is essential to breed from birds with large, globular crests. Usually some ducklings will be hatched without crests. Although these birds, when mature, will breed *crested* progeny, they are better discarded as breeders. Indeed, for breeding, the largest crests **should be present** although some breeders will state that the presence of a large crest on both sides is unnecessary.

Apparently the crested variety has lethal genes which can result in approximately 25% dead in shell. This means that a larger number of eggs must be set to obtain the number of ducklings required.

Care should be taken when rearing the ducklings with large crests. Some breeders suggest that the youngsters may be frightened by their crests and rush around, thus causing injury to themselves. If this happens, the fluff may be clipped from the scalp.

Provided care is taken the first few days, there should be no difficulty in rearing Crested ducks which are quite hardy.

EXHIBITION REQUIREMENTS

As indicated earlier, the Crested duck is a dual purpose breed, a fact which should be considered when judging. A laying duck should be alert and not overweight; yet it should be plump with enough meat to make it worthy of being a table bird.

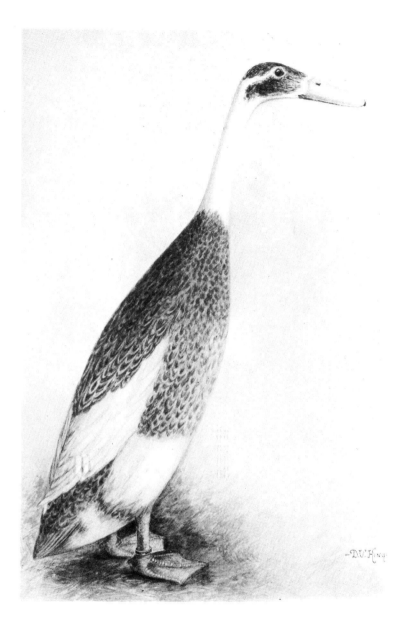

Figure 11.1 Fawn and White Indian Runner Duck. (From a drawing by D.W. Kingwell.)

Chapter 11

INDIAN RUNNER DUCKS

ORIGINS

The original source of Indian Runners was, of course, India, being brought to Whitehaven in Cumbria by a sea captain around 1850*. Later imports were also made and at the end of the 19th century their popularity spread.

According to one writer (J. Stephen Hicks, *Encyclopaedia of Poultry*) the true Indian Runners were developed by a Mr. J. Donald of Wigton, Cumbria and it was from this original stock that the present day stock are descended.

The same writer and other authorities have suggested that the breed came from the *true* **Penguin ducks** (now extinct)†.

Significantly, the older poultry books do not mention Indian Runners. Instead there is reference to the Penguin duck. W.B. Tegetmeier (*The Poultry Book*) refers to this duck in the following terms:

*In *British Poultry Standards* the origin is given as being Malaya not India, but other references state India.
†A Penguin duck does apparently exist but its precise origins are not clear. Whether bred from the same species is certainly not clear without further evidence becoming available.

Figure 11.2 Indian Runner Ducks exhibiting faulty carriage
(From *Races of Domestic Poultry*, Edward Brown)

"This very extraordinary-looking duck is characterized by an extreme shortness of the femora, the thigh or upper bones of the legs; hence their feet are not brought, as in other ducks, under the middle of the body, at an equal distance from the head and tail, but are placed much farther behind. In consequence of this peculiarity

of structure, the duck, in order to bring the centre of gravity over the point of support, is obliged to assume an erect attitude, like that of the Penguin, or other diving birds whose feet are placed in the same position.

"Beyond this quaint peculiarity, the Penguin duck has no speciality to call for particular observation, or to distinguish it from the ordinary species, of which it is evidently only an accidental variation, perpetuated by the care of man. The colours of the Penguin duck are varied, and the bird breeds freely with any of the common varieties."

The reason for the name is self-apparent. No other duck more resembles a penguin in its manner of standing and walking.

MAIN FEATURES

Indian Runners are egg laying birds and many believe they are *the* principal laying breed. However, when commercial laying trials were held the Khaki Campbells surpassed all others and for that reason they tend to be more popular than the Runners. Nevertheless, the latter are still quite popular and attract much attention when seen at shows.

In size they weigh around $3\frac{1}{2}$ to 5 lb, drakes being heavier than ducks. Accordingly, they do not require the same food intake as the larger breeds. Added to this benefit is the fact that they will forage for a considerable quantity of food, looking for titbits under leaves and other possible hiding places.

Good strains lay well in excess of 200 eggs per annum. The eggs are white in colour and around the size of a hen's egg (approximately $2\frac{1}{2}$ oz, 70.88g)

Although they have small bodies they can still be used as table birds. Many regard them as being well flavoured, somewhat similar to the wild duck. Obviously, though, the smallness does not make them suitable for family catering.

91

EXHIBITION REQUIREMENTS

The main characteristic of the Indian Runner is it upright body. This should be held at an angle of 65 to 75 degrees and in the U.S.A. top specimens are required to have a 90 degree carriage. The *British Poultry Standard* states that any carriage below 40 degrees should be regarded as a serious

Figure 11.3   Fawn and White Runner Duck showing the markings
(From *Feathered World* print)

defect but this allows poor specimens still to appear among the prize winners.

When the Indian Runner Club was in existence the *standard* specified the following:

	Points
Body shape and carriage	45
Head and neck	30
Colour markings and condition	25
	100

Today the Poultry Club expect body, carriage and overall action to be allocated 65 points thus emphasising the importance given to *type* characteristics.

Figure 11.4   Indian Runners – a group of pure whites at front
(*Photo courtesy:* Anita-Dawn Allen)

Colours
There are many colours although not all are listed in
British Poultry Standards. The main colours are as follows:

1. **Black** – Metallic black with green sheen. Black bill
   and legs, although dark fawn legs are per-
   mitted. Eyes should be dark coloured
   (brown).
2. **White** – Pure white with orange-yellow bill and
   legs. The eyes should be blue.
3. **Chocolate** – Dark chocolate plumage with black bill
   and legs. The duck should be a slightly
   lighter colour than the drake. The eyes
   should be brown.
4. **Fawn** – Body colour a warm even fawn, but the
   drake has a head and neck of bronze colour
   tinged with green. Bill and legs black, but
   olive green bill mottled with black permit-
   ted.
5. **Fawn and White** – Sections of fawn and white (see
   Fig. 11.1) with the drake having cap and
   cheek markings of bronze green. Legs and
   feet are orange-red whereas the bill is
   "cucumber" in the duck and green-yellow in
   the drake.

Notes

(a) There are detailed variations in the fawn and fawn
and white colours. In the ducks the feathers are "double
laced" with the inner centre being dark and the outer mar-
gin having a lighter tinge. With the drakes the feathers are
pencilled with darkish lines. This pencilling should be very

94

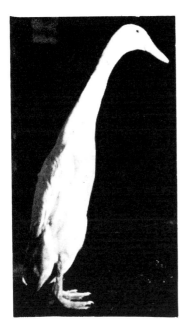

Figure 11.5 **Above**: An attractive White Runner
Bottom: A mixed pen of Runners

Pole & thatch sun shade

Figure 11.6　Indian Runner Duck – a group of Blacks and Whites
(*Photo courtesy:* Anita-Dawn Allen)

faint or minute so that it is hardly discernible. For a detailed analysis of colour the reader is referred to the *British Poultry Standards*. In the U.S.A. the Fawn and White is known as the **Pencilled Variety**.

(b) Many "off colours" also exist and many more could be produced. However, this is discouraged by official bodies. *

Major faults

The importance of "type" has already been noted. Accordingly, any deviations from the typical bird should be penalised. Examples are as follows:

1. Horizontal body.
2. Oversized or too small.
3. Uncharacteristic walk or gait; i.e. waddling.
4. Head which is domed or too large.
5. Bill which is dished.
6. Neck too thick or not curved.
7. Legs wrongly positioned.
8. Colours which are not according to the *standard*.

Examples

(a) **Fawns** – any other "foreign" colour in the plumage. Light colour in bill.

(b) **Blacks** – white in plumage; lack of metallic green on plumage; green bills; lacing; wrong colour legs.

(c) **Chocolate** – colour too light or patchy; wrong colour bill.

(d) **Fawn and white** – colours not confined to areas specified (see Fig. 11.1); lack of pencilling or lacing; white circle around eye not distinct.

*These include Mallard, Cumberland Blue and Trout Coloured. Because this duck is of 'mixed' colours many other varieties will emerge, but they do not justify standardization .

A CHALLENGE

The Indian Runner offers considerable scope to the fancier who wants a utility duck with tremendous interest value. Top class specimens can be bred and improvements can be made year-by-year. Breeding the standardised colours presents a great and fascinating challenge.

Figure 12.1   Front view of Muscovy Drake

(*Photo:* Vandyck Studios)

Chapter 12

MUSCOVY DUCKS

ORIGINS

This duck appears to be rather unique. Unlike other ducks, which originated from the wild Mallard, the Muscovy comes from the Wild Musk duck which is found in the warmer regions of South America such as Paraguay and Guiana.

Earlier writers such as Caius and Willoughby mention this duck by the name of Turkish and Brazilian duck respectively. But many other names have also been used. The "Musk duck" may have been one of its names and gradually that became "Muscovy". Possibly the name came from the odour of the skin of the birds.

The fact that the Muscovy does not appear to interbreed freely with other species of duck would also confirm that this duck is from a separate race. In the experience of the author no breeding has been done with other types of duck even though running with Muscovies. Other writers have stated that crosses have been possible, but the offspring have been sterile.

Some writers have stated that the Muscovy should be really classified as a goose rather than a duck. However, the

99

breed more resembles a duck than a goose and it is usual to classify them as ducks. Darrel Sheraw (*Successful Duck and Goose Raising*, Stromberg, Pine River, Minnesota, U.S.A.) puts forward the view that the Muscovy is developed from the Wild Pato of South America. However, this Pato could well be the Musk duck mentioned earlier.

UTILITY PROPERTIES

Muscovies lay reasonably well and the eggs are an acceptable size, although not very large for the weight of the duck which is in the region of 5-7 lb. They are not in the same class as Pekins for laying, but they are good grazers and foragers, thus helping to keep down the amount of food which has to be supplied.

They are very hardy and require no special attention. Indeed, left to themselves they will hatch their own eggs and rear the ducklings. The latter fatten quite well, although somewhat slowly compared with the Aylesbury or Pekin. If drakes are kept on they will grow to 12 lb or even more, but if left too long the flesh becomes tough and, of course, the food intake for a number of drakes can be quite large. Preferably they should be killed before 6 months of age.

Drakes are often very pugnacious. They will tolerate no opposition so other fowl are best run separately unless they are in a field or paddock. The author had a drake which could quickly flatten all opposition – even a game cock – by simply using his strong wings and superior weight.

Periodically they take to the wing and fly around, often landing on the top of a shed to survey their territory. They are strong fliers and slow deliberate walkers. However, the drake will often thrust his head forward and then back making him look quite ferocious. Whether this is a mating

100

Figure 12.2   Muscovy Drake – side view

display or simply a method of the drake showing his superiority is not clear.

The incubation period is longer than that taken by other ducks being 35 days and not the normal 28 days. The duck is a very keen broody and will prevent anyone trying to take the eggs from under her. The ducklings hatch fairly quickly: they emerge with a variety of markings; yellow and black being the main colours.

Figure 12.3   Muscovy Drake – standing

(*Photo:* Vandyck Studios)

Figure 12.4 Possible Methods of Semi-Intensive Rearing once off heat. Top: Sun Parlour & Slatted floor (avoids wet bedding); Bottom: Wire Floors. Once feathered can be let out during the day.

As a meat duck there is no doubt that the Muscovy has much to offer. The meat is succulent and quite tasty. On drakes especially there is a plentiful supply of breast meat which is dark in colour. In olden times, more than 200 years or more ago, the Muscovy was highly regarded as a dish for special feasts.

When handling a Muscovy great care should be taken with the foot claws; these are extremely sharp and can inflict a rather unpleasant cut which may quickly become inflamed.

EXHIBITION REQUIREMENTS

The Muscovy is a utility duck and should be judged in that category. Essential features are as follows:

1. Horizontal carriage.
2. Large body, both long and broad with prominent breast.
3. Strong, short legs.
4. Strong wings.
5. Long tail carried low and no curled feathers in the drake.
6. Colours – combinations of black, white and sometimes blue; chocolates have also been created.
7. Face covered with red, bare patches of flesh known as caruncles – very pronounced in the male. In fact it is the large caruncle and greater size which distinguishes the drake from the duck.
8. On the male long feathers on the head in the form of a crest which he raises when agitated.
9. Legs should be appropriate to the colour of the bird varying from yellow for a pure white bird to black for the very dark ducks.

Figure 12.5 White Muscovy and duckling

Faults

The Muscovy is a vigorous duck and in the drake there is a positive aggressiveness which should show in his appearance. Any sign of weakness should be penalised. Points to cover or faults to be found are as follows:

1. Small body and wrong type of carriage.
2. Head faults such as:
   (a) Too much or too little caruncle.
   (b) No crest on male.
   (c) Bill too long or the wrong shape.
3. Long legs.
4. Broken and badly worn feathers. Muscovies do not have the same oil content in their feathers as other ducks and, therefore, their condition may deteriorate more quickly.

SHOW PREPARATION

Given a good grass run with a small area of swimming water the Muscovy will thrive and keep clean. They are best kept in a small field or paddock surrounded by wire netting to keep them from roaming. A reasonably large area allows them to fly around regularly and the grass keeps the plumage in good condition.

A shed should be provided in which the ducks can be locked in late in the evening. Otherwise they may fly on to fences or other structures and be caught by a fox the following morning.

Chapter 13

ORPINGTONS

ORIGINS

That great poultry breeder William Cook of St. Mary Cray, Kent created the Orpington duck. Strangely, in his book *Ducks and How to Make Them Pay* (4th ed. c. 1895) he makes no reference to his new creation, but by 1921 the breed was well established and included in the Poultry Club *Standards*.

Edward Brown writing in 1906 does not refer to the breed (*Races of Domestic Poultry*, Arnold, London) so it is very clear that the creation had not been made public. T.W. Sturges (*The Poultry Manual*, 1909) acknowledges that the Orpington duck had been introduced so it would appear that they were made known to the public in the years 1907-1909.

The aim of the breeder, William Cook, was to produce a buff coloured duck at a time when this colour was all the rage; in fact, a fashion or fad. At the same time the hope appears to have been to produce a utility bird, heavy enough to be a table bird and yet an acceptable layer.

The formula required was a laying duck crossed with the heavier breeds and then, by careful selection, to achieve the desired colour and utility properties. Apparently he experimented with Indian Runners crossing in turn with Aylesbury, Rouen and Cayugas until the buff colour was achieved. With the infusion of Indian Runner blood the laying average was pushed up and a medium-heavy duck was produced (6-7 lb) which yet could be ready for market at 8 to 10 weeks.

A Blue Orpington was produced from the Buff. Some suggest that the Blue Swedish duck was used to strengthen the blue colour.

UTILITY PROPERTIES

The Orpington has much to offer the breeder who is look-ing for an attractive duck which has combined utility prop-erties of satisfactory laying and rapid conversion of flesh. It will be apparent that the more eggs produced by a duck, combined with a high level of fertility, the greater the possible output from a breeding pen. From the best strains more than 200 eggs per annum have been obtained.

Figure 13.1 Buff Orpington Ducks

EXHIBITION REQUIREMENTS

The Orpington should have a fairly large body as befits a table bird yet without visible signs of a keel. The carriage should be slightly upright, but certainly not as pronounced as the Indian Runner or even the Pekin.

The neck should be of medium length and is slightly curved. This should be graced by a head which is fine and oval in shape with a bill which is moderately long, placed in a straight line from the skull.

Wings should be strong and wrapped closely around the body. The tail should be small with a gentle upturn. The plumage should be "hard feathered".

Legs and bill should be orange with the former having a distinct red tinge. The eye should be brown with a blue iris.

In colour the Buff should be a sound, even buff colour throughout. The drake's head should be a glossy seal-brown colour (*British Poultry Standards*). However, in the U.S.A. a completely self colour has been bred even in the drake and some think this more desirable.

The Blue Orpington no longer appears to be around or, at least, is not common. The colour should be a dark – yet clear – blue with a white bib. The bill and legs are blue with possibly orange mottling.

Faults
The faults of the Orpington relate to type and colour. Examples are as follows:

1. Small size.
2. Horizontal or very upright carriage.
3. Short body or defects in body such as:
   (a) roach backed;

The Buff Orpington Duck.

Right & wrong Types.

Correct shape
and carriage.
Long and deep body.
Alert clean head.
"Well balanced"
Eggs & Meat.

Heavy and dull.
Coarse "dished" head.
short, thick neck
"Roach back."
Pronounced Keel.
Table use only.

Too near to
Runner type.
No depth and
badly balanced.
Eggs possibly, but
poor capacity.

a.ms.

Figure 13.2   Buff Orpington – created by William Cook – showing standard type

110

(b) pronounced keel.
4. Imperfect colouring:
   (a) drake with wrong colouring on head such as grey or blue;
   (b) uneven colouring or existence of lacing;
   (c) reversion of colour such as found in Rouen or in Mallard;
   (d) white wing feathers;
   (e) eyes, bill or legs wrong colour.

SHOW PREPARATION

Being a colour breed there is a necessity to keep birds out of strong sunlight which will fade the "deep re-buff" required by the *standard*. Adequate washing water should be provided. The food given should contain oil and other proteins and, therefore, for keeping birds in condition layers' pellets are recommended.

This breed is worthy of a larger following and hopefully with the growing interest in ducks they will be taken up more.

Figure 14.1   Pekin Duck
Comparison of British (*Top*) and U.S.A. (*Bottom*)

Chapter 14

PEKIN DUCKS

ORIGIN

Without doubt the origin of the Pekin is as indicated by the name. The first imports were brought into England more than 100 years ago (1872) and arrived in the U.S.A., again from Peking, a year later.

Once established in Europe and the U.S.A. the breed established itself as a very popular table bird. Although not as popular in England as the Aylesbury, the Pekin is still acknowledged for its laying and meat-producing qualities. In the U.S.A. the commercial side of duck production is largely built around the Pekin.

MAIN FEATURES

The Pekin is a large duck which weighs between 7-9 lb, drakes and mature birds reaching the heavier weights. The carriage is more upright than the Aylesbury. Some writers suggest a body angle of 45 degrees above horizontal, but this is not a uniform stance. Although typical specimens are fairly upright there are positive variations to be found. Those in the U.S.A. are more horizontal than the British-

Figure 14.2   Pekin Duck showing standard type
   Top: Correct type
   Bottom: Type exhibiting a number of faults

114

type bird. This can be seen from the illustrations given in Figure 14.1.

Certainly the original type of Pekin was more upright than those now found in North America. Possibly the "horizontal" bodied bird has come about by a cross with the Aylesbury.

UTILITY PROPERTIES

The Pekin is a supreme table bird which lays very well for a heavy-type of duck. Eggs are white and generally of high quality. There is no problem with breeding even under intensive, commercial conditions.

Pekins fatten quickly, reaching around 5 lb in 11-12 weeks. This compares unfavourably with Aylesburys which mature at 8 weeks of age. Moreover, the flesh of the Pekin tends to be yellow, again a disadvantage compared with the Aylesbury. The better laying ability can obviously give the Pekin an edge over other heavy breeds.

EXHIBITION REQUIREMENTS

The Pekin has a large body which is broad and long. The British *Standard* specified **medium** length of body, but in practice this tends to be long. It is also fairly deep, but not as deep as the Aylesbury, although it will be appreciated that the difference in the angle of the body make the Aylesbury appear to have a much deeper keel.

The back of the Pekin is flat and the wings should be carried high and tightly around the body. The breast should be broad and full. The tail should be cocked upwards and not following the line of the back as in the Aylesbury or the Rouen. The paunch should be full and low.

The head of the Pekin should be broad and oval shaped. From the base of the strong bill the forehead curves upwards in a more pronounced fashion than the Rouen or Aylesbury. The neck should be broad and strong at the base and where it joins the head. With the cheeks broad and broad skull overhanging the eyes the effect is one of bulk and strength. Drakes have larger heads than ducks.

From the illustration given it will be seen that the bulk of the body is carried at the front of the legs. The latter should be strong, thighs being of medium length and shanks fairly short. Bill and legs should be bright orange and eyes should be a grey blue – usually referred to as "lead blue".

The colour of the abundant plumage is creamy white. This may vary from a distinct *yellowy*-white to almost pure white. Provided the colour is even throughout, without any black or other colour features, the precise shade of white is immaterial.

FAULTS

1. Deep keel.
2. Horizontal body.
3. Smallness of size.
4. Pale coloured or mis-coloured bill.
5. Wrong position of legs.
6. Wrong shape of head such as a flat crown or narrowness.
7. Lack of breadth in body.
8. Lacking beetle brows.
9. Slender neck lacking distinct curve.
10. Any feature which departs from the characteristic coarseness of the breed.

116

Figure 14.3   Pekin Drake (front) and Ducks

PREPARATION FOR SHOW

Pekins do not require *special* show preparation. However, it is essential to provide the following:

1. Swimming water even though limited. The essential requirement is to allow the birds water in which to wash themselves.
2. Ample food with an adequate protein requirement for adding flesh and maintaining health.
3. Feed maize and allow the ducks to run on grass; this keeps the yellow colour in the plumage and the bright orange in the legs and bill.

Chapter 15

ROUEN

PREMIER TABLE BIRD

The Rouen is a majestic bird. Large – *massive* is possibly more appropriate – and both male and female present a regal picture. In colour they follow the Mallard and as such they are one of the most attractive of all varieties of domesticated ducks.

This variety has been bred for well over a century under this name and previously was known as the "Rhone duck" after an area in France. Whether this is the origin of the name is uncertain. Some writers have suggested that the name came from Cardinal Rohan (the variety being named after him), or that the *colour* **roan**, a mixture of brown and grey, was the inspiration for the name. Whatever the derivation, the name Rouen is now accepted in Britain, the U.S.A. and other parts of the world.

The Rouen is the largest of ducks* – the *standard* specifies 9 lb ducks and 10 lb for drakes. In practice, drakes often achieve around 11 lb. Its flesh is better flavoured than other varieties, but requires more time to mature than its main competitor the Aylesbury.

* The Muscovy drake may achieve larger weights up to 14 lb, but the duck is around half this size.

119

DESCRIPTION

The head of the Rouen should be large and *round* with the bill being a natural continuation of the curve. This should be set on a fairly long neck which has a distinct curve.

A large body with deep keel is essential. The horizontal carriage without excessive fluff at the rear should give the impression of bulk without appearing clumsy or too fat.

In colour the **drake** is predominantly grey with brown-black lines across the shoulders. The breast is a rich claret colour leading up to a white ring ($\frac{1}{4}$ inch thick) at the base of the neck. Above this white ring the neck should be a sort of black-green all gleaming and lustrous (rich iridescent

Figure 15.1 Rouen Duck   (From *Our Poultry*, Harrison Weir)

120

green). Across each wing is a blue band with, at each end, a black line and a white line side by side (see illustration).

The **duck** is predominantly a rich mahogany brown, each body feather being pencilled with dark brown or black. The wing band is similar to that for the drake.

There are black lines down the head and around the eyes.

The bill of the duck is bright orange, whereas that of the drake should be greenish yellow.

The legs and webs are dark orange (duck) or an orange red (drake); for the latter the *standard* states: "bright brick red" but often this is somewhat faded.

In the summer months the *drake* takes similar plumage to that of the duck.

EXHIBITION REQUIREMENTS

For exhibition the Rouen must comply with the *standard* particularly for **size, colour**, and **type**. Do not expect a small bird to win because this requirement of size is absolutely vital

Fortunately, as regards colour, Rouens breed quite true.

Faults

The Rouen should be a massive duck and any feature which detracts from this principal requirement should be frowned upon and, where serious, should be penalised by judges.

Small, under-sized bodies lacking front and deep keel would not comply with the *standard*. On poorer specimens the front of the keel curves up from the legs, giving a good clearance from the ground. This curved line may result in a pleasing looking bird, but this does not mean compliance with top show needs.

The wrong colour in duck or drake would be regarded as a serious fault. The absence of the steel blue wing bar in the drake, or dark or white feathers appearing in the wrong places, are examples. Sometimes a white ring appears on the neck of the duck and this is a fault. The wrong colour of bill is also a common failing; early books specified "leaden green bills" as a defect and certainly any colour bill other than bright green-yellow (drakes) or orange (ducks) would be unacceptable.

UTILITY PROPERTIES

The Rouen achieves the same size as the Aylesbury, but is not as widely kept for the following reasons:

1. **Mature Slowly**
   Whereas the Aylesbury will be ready for the table at 7 or 8 weeks old, although not fully grown, the Rouen takes much longer to fill out. Indeed, it may be 7 months or longer before a Rouen duck is ready for killing and eating.
2. **Dark Feathers**
   The dark stubs left on the Rouen detract from what would otherwise be an attractive roasting duck. However, once cooked there is little difference between the dark feathered and white feathered birds.
3. **Poor Fertility**
   Some breeders have suggested that the top, show-type Rouen is a difficult bird to breed from. The heavy, low-built frame is not conducive to an active life. Nevertheless, provided yearling drakes are used with not more than 3 ducks for each male no

122

Figure 15.2 Massive pair of Rouens resting near a pond

problems should be experienced.

Many matters affect fertility: food, greenstuff, exercise, fresh air, age of stock, and other environmental factors.

Prime quality

For those who want a duck with abundant flesh of a fine and delicate flavour the Rouen is unsurpassed. Reared on grass with adequate food the steady growth produces food fit for the gourmet.

The flesh of the Rouen is darker than the Aylesbury and has a "gamey" flavour similar to the Mallard. At 8 months old a weight of around 8-10 lb is possible and exceptionally larger birds may be produced.

The eggs are pale green in colour and quite a good size (3½ oz, 99 g). Some strains lay a reasonable number, but do *not* expect a star performance. They are meat ducks not prolific egg layers.

Although the dark features may be cited as a disadvantage, yet the Rouen is one of the most beautiful ducks. Its glossy plumage, particularly on the drake, provides a splendid sight. Majestically they forage in an orchard, paddock or other enclosure. With the sun shining across their backs they look magnificent, yet graceful and tranquil. The dark plumage does not get soiled easily and, therefore, lasts so much longer. Yet the white duck has great problems. The plumage becomes yellow and soiled and there is great difficulty in keeping the bill a pale colour.

ROUEN CLAIR

A variety named the Rouen Clair is now included in the *Standards* : this is a smaller bird with a more upright carriage, but longer than the Rouen. The colour is similar to the Mallard. It would appear to be the same as the Duclair–Rouen covered later (p135).

Chapter 16

OTHER VARIETIES OF DUCKS

There are many other ducks which could be mentioned. Some are now quite rare or even extinct, others have lost favour and are in very few hands. Nevertheless, because fashions change there is always a hope that some of these ducks will re-appear, just as many of the breeds of domestic fowl have been revived in recent years.

BLUE SWEDISH

Origins
The Blue Swedish is a very old breed which has been known in Europe for generations, possibly originating in Germany. However, it was brought to this country from Sweden hence the name given. They were later imported to the U.S.A. and apparently are now fairly popular.

Utility Properties
This duck is a utility breed which matures fairly slowly and provides excellent meat. They are said to be well flavoured with a wide distribution of flesh.

The special flavour may be attributed to the fact that the

Blue Swedish prefers to have a reasonable sized orchard or paddock in which they can forage, the grass and natural food assisting in the development of the succulent flesh. In confinement they do not thrive so well.

Exhibition Requirements
The Blue Swedish duck is similar in some respects to both the Pekin and Rouen. Its body is similar to the Pekin, but has the carriage, though not size, of the Rouen. The long body should be broad breasted and well balanced on strong legs. The weight is around 7 lb.

Figure 16.1   Blue Swedish Duck

In colour the Blue Swedish is a slate-blue with black. The bib is white and the legs orange white whereas the bill should be olive green for the drake and somewhat browner in the duck. However, in the U.S.A. the *standard* calls for a bill of "greenish blue", but the British *Standard* is probably more realistic.

Faults
Smallness of body, lack of breast, faulty legs, faded colours and too much white are all examples of faults which should be penalised.

Figure 16.2   Typical Magpie Duck

127

MAGPIE

Origins and Utility

The Magpie is said to have originated in Wales. Weighing around 5 -7 lb, drakes being the heavier, it is a utility duck which lays quite well. Being basically a white duck the Magpie has white flesh which gives it a distinct advantage for table purposes.

Exhibition Requirements

The Magpie is a very long bodied bird with a long strong neck and a broad head of good length. A long bill is also essential. The main colour is white with a black cap, shoulders and remainder of back, including the side of the tail. The bill is yellow to orange and the legs and feet are orange.

This unusual breed is available in the U.S.A., but alas appears to be very rare in Britain.

SAXONY DUCKS*

Origins

This utility breed was developed in the early 1930s as a farmyard duck. As would be expected from a bird which has an ancestry of Rouen, German Pekin and Blue Pommeranian this is a fairly heavy breed which fattens very well.

In recent years there has been renewed interest in the breed and they are wide spread in East Germany. They are rare in other countries with a few breeders in Britain.

The breed is noted for its very attractive plumage. The **drake** is a light oatmeal colour on the lower part of the body, the breast and shoulders are rusty red and the head and

*Based on notes kindly supplied by Mrs. Lorna Heard.

128

Figure 16.3   Saxony Ducks
Top: Saxony Ducks and Drakes
Bottom: Saxony Ducks   *(Courtesy:* Mrs. Lorna Heard)

129

neck are blue grey. The **duck** is buff colour, darker on head, neck and breast than the rest of the body. They both present an extremely attractive picture.

Utility Properties
Saxonies are very presentable performers, as layers averaging around 160 eggs per annum. The size of the egg usually exceeds $2\frac{3}{4}$ oz.

They are broad breasted and built as table ducks, the drakes achieving around 8 lb and ducks 1 lb less.

Exhibition Requirements
From a side view the Saxony resembles the Pekin. However, its carriage should be almost horizontal and any sign of an upright carriage, apparent with some strains of Pekin, would be regarded as a fault.

The detailed *standard* which is applied in East Germany is reproduced below.

Recognised Standard
Carriage: almost horizontal, leaning slightly backward.
Type: body long, broad and deep, without a keel. The wings are medium length and carried close into the sides. The tail is full and held in a horizontal position. Drakes have two or three curled feathers above the tail.
Head: long and flat. The neck is average length and not too thin. The eyes are dark brown. The drake's bill is yellow, and may be tinged with green. The duck's bill is browny yellow.
Legs: medium length, with fine bones. They are set almost in the middle of the body, and are orange in colour.
Plumage: lies close to the body. The down is pale cream.

Colour of egg shell: white. **Weight of egg**: more than $2\frac{3}{4}$ oz.
Colour: **Drake**: The head and neck are blue grey as far as the neck ring, which is white. The breast and shoulders are rusty red with slight silver lacing. The lower back and rump are blue grey. The rest of the body, the tail and curled feathers, and the rings are oat-meal coloured, the wings being tinged with blue.
Colour: **Duck**: the head, neck and breast are buff, which becomes paler over the rest of the body. There is a conspicuous cream streak above the eyes, and a slight broken neck ring of the same colour. The wing coverts and tail are pale grey.
Defects: Broken neck ring, in the drake. Pale eyes. Upright walk. Dark coloured nostrils. Dark under feathers.
Economic qualities: Saxonies are good layers, considering their size, about 160 eggs a year. The quality of their flesh is excellent. They grow rapidly and make a full breasted meaty carcass. The adult drake weighs about 8 lb, and the duck 7 lb.

OTHER BREEDS

Other breeds which have existed and may still exist but in small numbers in the U.K. are as follows:

1. **Bali Duck**
The Bali looks rather like an Indian Runner duck, but with the addition of a small, rather compact, crest.

Obviously it should stand upright like the Indian Runner. The weight is around 4 lb for ducks and 5 lb for drakes.

The Bali probably originated from the Isle of Bali on the Java Coast. They are pure white in colour, with bill and feet of orange red, and blue eyes.

2. Baldwin Duck

This breed was standardised but regretfully is no longer seen. In size drakes are around 10 lb and ducks 1 lb lighter. The plumage is rather similar to the Rouen, but the colours are not exactly the same.

3. Silver Appleyard Ducks*

This was a breed created by Reginald Appleyard who was an enthusiastic duck and goose breeder who died in 1964. It was created in a *standard* size as well as a *bantam* version.

The colour of the drake is rather like the Mallard but with a paler body. The duck has a background colour of white,

*For an interesting article on origins and Reginald Appleyard see the B.W.A. *Waterfowl Year Book and Buyers Guide 1976-77*

Figure 16.4   Drawing of Bali Duck

streaked with grey and fawn. The appearance being of *silver* – hence the name. Their make-up would appear to be Mallard, White Campbells and possibly Rouen, but this cannot be confirmed.

As layers they are apparently very good and the eggs are fairly large. Moreover, they are hardy and breed easily.

Little is known on the origin of the bantam version but it is certainly a very attractive duck.

4. Welsh Harlequin Ducks

The originator of the Welsh Harlequin duck is Group Captain Leslie Bonnet. The breed first came as a sport from Khaki Campbells and then by careful breeding the new breed was stabilised. Apparently the eggs tend to be larger and the Welsh Harlequins are an easily managed bird.

As shown in the photograph they are lighter in colour than the Khaki Campbells.

Standard

General Characteristics – Both sexes

Carriage is sprightly, slightly upright, head held high, back sloping gently from shoulder to saddle. The keel is well clear of the ground for active foraging. Body is compact with width well maintained from stem to stern. Tail short and small. Drakes have the usual curled tail feathers. Head is fine-drawn. Neck is almost vertical and medium in length.

Colour: Drakes

Head and neck beetle-green to within an inch of the shoulders, where a ring $\frac{1}{2}$ inch wide and pure white completely encircles the neck. In all other respects also, except in size, the drake is coloured just the same as its Mallard counter-

133

Figure 16.5   Pair of Silver Appleyards (large)
(*Courtesy:* Charles & Maggie Piper, Alford Acre)

part. The bill is gunmetal coloured; shanks orange.

Colour: Ducks

Head and neck fawn, turning paler with age. Rest of the body is basically cream with tortoiseshell effect in cream and blue on back and wings. Bars on wings are electric blue, or green. Bills are yellow or gunmetal.

Weights   Drakes – 5½-6 lb
              Ducks – 5 lb

134

5. Duclair-Rouen Duck

The Duclair-Rouen appears to be a close relative of the Rouen described earlier. The breed is of French origin. Apparently the ducks are extremely good layers and quick growers, being very similar to Aylesburys in this respect. Their plumage is similar to the Rouen, but not as bright. Distinctive features are the white neck and breast.

In shape it resembles the Rouen, but is not quite as heavy, mature drakes being around 9 lb and ducks 8 lb. The bill is almost black in the duck and dark green in the drake.

6. Blue Termonde Duck

The Blue Termonde originates from Belgium. According to Edward Brown (*Races of Domestic Poultry*) blue ducks, which are a slate-grey colour, have been in the United Kingdom for generations. However, whether he is implying a connection between these Blues and the Blue Termonde is not clear.

In shape they are similar to the Blue Swedish, being quite long in the body as well as being broad. However, in weight they are substantial being around 8 to 10 lb the drakes being heavier than the ducks.

The colour is a blue-grey slate colour with dark lacing.

The medium length legs should be a dark colour – reddy brown mixed with black, and the longish bill should be blue in colour.

7. Huttegem Duck

The Huttegem may be the result of crossing the Blue Termonde with a lighter bodied duck, possibly a Runner. The result is a duck which is of medium size yet which combines good laying qualities and excellent table properties.

Apparently the duckling are extremely hardy and good

Figure 16.6   Welsh Harlequin Duck
(*Courtesy:* Group Captain Leslie Bonnet)

Figure 16.7   Welsh Harlequin Drake
(*Courtesy:* Group Captain Leslie Bonnet)

136

foragers. This means they can be reared quite easily and when required for roasting may be killed at around 9 weeks of age.

In colour they may be blue, tawny or dark fawn.

8. Coaley Fawn Duck

The Coaley Fawn ducks were originated by a Miss Edwards of Gloucestershire, being intended to be extremely good layers as well as having a plump body of medium size. In other words, this was an attempt to obtain the laying abilities of the Indian Runner with a bird that was also good for the table.

In colour they should be fawn with the drakes having a chocolate-coloured head as a distinguishing feature.

Regretfully this breed appears to be very rare if not extinct.

9. Abacot Ranger

This is a breed similar to the Siver Appleyard in appearance which was produced by crossing the White Sports from Khaki Campbells with a White Indian Runner drake and then by careful selection the breed was evolved. This occurred around 1923 and although successful as a layer lost favour.

The breed was taken up in Germany where it still exists and is standardized.

The duck is white in colour with fawn markings. The head is fawn and so are the back and wings. The drake has also a white ground colour, but the dark markings are more distinct. In carriage they are similar to the Khaki Campbells.

* From details given by Jonathan M Thompson who has been responsible for reviving interest in the breed in the UK.

Figure 16.8 Abacot Rangers (Courtesy: J M Thompson)

Figure 16.9 Huttegem Duck

Chapter 17

DUCKLINGS FOR THE TABLE

CASE FOR DUCKLINGS

Essential requirements for any livestock intended for the table are as follows:

1. Relatively easy to rear
2. Good conversion rate of food into meat
3. Do not suffer from many diseases or other hazards
4. At the end of a reasonable time they can be killed
5. There is a ready demand for the finished product

Ducklings meet all these requirements, provided they are the table variety. The Aylesbury, Pekin and Rouen come into this category. At ten weeks of age each is capable of achieving around 6-8 lb with heavier weights when special feeding is used.

The growth of ducklings running in a garden, orchard or small paddock is always a source of great amazement. If any-one doubts this statement, hatch chickens and ducklings during the same week, feed exactly the same food, and then compare the progress of the two species. After one week the difference will be apparent, the ducklings then continuing to grow at more than twice the rate achieved by the chicks.

139

If a broody hen is used as a mother the ducklings will become independent very quickly. The poor "mother" must be very puzzled to see her brood grow so quickly and ignore her attentions. In mild weather they will not require heat after about ten days. However, watch for frosty nights and make sure the ducklings are locked up each night where they are sheltered.

GOOD START ESSENTIAL

A high protein food is essential for quick and sustained growth. Chick crumbs may be used or, alternatively, a method employed with great success by the author, is to feed on **turkey starter crumbs**. These are more expensive than ordinary chick crumbs, but they give excellent results.

After a few weeks some different food should be introduced. Grain soaked in water is quite good. Layers pellets or layers crumbs are excellent for fattening and so are the special "crumbs" formulated for the purpose; e.g. broiler crumbs or pellets.

The main advantages of feeding with pellets, using a gravity hopper, is that the ducklings can "shovel" up the food; there is no waste, and labour costs are kept to a minimum. However, the price of compounded food is high and for this reason the poultry keeper who has time available may prefer to mix the food, incorporating household scraps.

Foods which may be used to great advantage are as follows:

1. Ground oats.
2. Barley meal.
3. Boiled rice.

4. Potatoes (when available at a low price).
5. Bread soaked in water or milk.
6. Food scraps boiled.

The aim should be to produce a "crumbly" mash. Accordingly, the dry oats or meal would be mixed with the "boilings" to the correct consistency. A compromise is to use layers' mash (dry meal) mixed with the household scraps.

Remember that a high quality food will fatten quickly. Try to reduce the protein value too much and the build up of flesh will suffer.

Figure 17.1 Device for Watering Ducklings

141

Green stuff is essential. If ducklings are able to forage in a grass enclosure or orchard they will eat the natural greenstuff and thereby obtain great benefit. Cabbage, lawn clippings, chick weed, and leaves from trees in the autumn all provide excellent supplementary food.

Drinking water is essential from the first day. A drinking fountain is quite adequate. Later it will be found that the ducklings will enjoy a shallow pool – an inverted dustbin lid or old sink will suffice – in which to clean themselves. However, a deep pond is *not* essential.

The *situation* of the drinking appliance is important. Placed on soil with no protection, the area will very quickly become waterlogged and muddy. Accordingly, it is advisable to employ flag stones or design a special surround and drain.

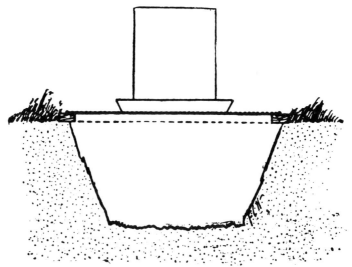

Figure 17.2   Cross-section of Watering Device showing drainage

ADVANTAGES CLAIMED FOR DUCKLINGS

W. Powell Owen a prolific writer on poultry matters in the hey day of small holdings claimed twenty advantages for ducklings (from *Duck Keeping on Money Making Lines*, now out of print).

1. No grain is needed.
2. No swimming water is required.
3. The sexes do not have to be separated (drakes do not fight).
4. Ducklings mature much quicker than chicks.
5. Expensive housing and equipment are unnecessary.
6. Cheap and coarse feeds can be used.
7. Ducklings will gobble up all waste greenstuff.
8. If necessary, expensive foods such as grain and cereals can be avoided altogether.
9. Large flocks can be reared in small enclosures.
10. Existing outbuildings can be utilized for fattening sheds.
11. Cheap shelters can be constructed.
12. Ducklings can be weaned at a very early age.
13. Rapid production is possible throughout the season as the stocks can be turned constantly due to the ducklings fattening so quickly.
14. Breeding stock can be run in large flocks with a number of drakes.
15. If suitable "pasture" is available the breeding stock can forage and find a great deal of their food from March to September.

143

16. Ducklings are not mischievous among growing crops like chickens.
17. A very high wire netting fence is unnecessary.
18. Low boards can be used instead of netting.
19. Ducklings can be reared with very little heat.
20. The feathers can be sold at a good profit.

Most of these advantages still apply. Possibly number seventeen requires modification for certain ducks. When fully developed, powerful ducks like the Muscovy can fly quite high. The author has seen them perch on top of a shed 8 to 9 feet high, so a very low fence may not keep them enclosed. Although wing clipping or pinioning is possible, this practice is not to be recommended for domesticated ducks. They are tame creatures, who should be treated as birds of the household, and not as semi-wild birds.

CONFINEMENT

The smallholder who wishes to fatten a few ducks will find that ducks thrive well on grass – which gives adequate green stuff – provided they are not allowed to run off the weight which is gained. Reasonable exercise, fresh air and avoiding contamination of ground and water are all essential.

Train ducklings to go into a shed each night. Surprisingly they only need to be shown the way a few times and they then find their own way. This is better for their health and certainly cuts down the possibility of losses from prowlers such as cats, dogs and foxes. Usually these appear very easily and, therefore, overnight locking of a duck house can avoid trouble.

Shavings, grass clippings or leaves can be used for bedding. A hopper full of pellets can be kept in the duck house, thus allowing feeding to take place even when the ducklings are closed up.

The aim should be to feed in a manner which develops ducklings as quickly as possible. Usually they are killed at around eight to ten weeks old. As this stage weights should be approximately 8 lb, with the really good table birds such as Aylesbury reaching 10 lb or more.

Figure 17.3   Ducklings *(Courtesy:* Dr. Anderson Brown, *The Incubation Book)*

GOOD RECIPES

The choice of food depends very much upon how much the duck keeper wishes to spend and the related aspect – the time available for preparing special recipes. Ready formulated and prepared pellets keep labour costs to a minimum and allows *ad lib* feeding – essential for quick growth.

On the other hand, *variety* and attractive, palatable foods, such as wet mashes, may induce ducks to eat *more* and thereby increase weight more quickly. Such mixtures or recipes require preparation and a certain amount of guesswork. If deprived of protein the ducklings may not fatten; yet an excessive amount is costly and wasteful. Fortunately with free range birds the *precise* formulation is not critical; in spring, summer and autumn ducklings will forage for snails, slugs, worms and greenstuff.

Recipes for early maturity

Recipe No. 1

Week 1   Hard boiled eggs (chopped fine)
Breadcrumbs
Boiled rice (limited amounts) to be mixed with milk

Week 2   Barley meal
Onwards   Bran
Oatmeal
Maize meal
Middlings
Rice
Meat (shredded)

146

These should be steamed or boiled and then fed at intervals throughout the day. The proportions should be as indicated below for Recipe No. 2.

Recipe No. 2

		Parts
Week 1	Biscuit meal	8
	Weatings	40
	Barley meal	20
	Ground oats	20
	Dried milk	10
	Cod liver oil	2
		100

Week 2	Weatings	25
Onwards	Barley meal	30
	Ground oats	30
	Meat and Bone Meal	10
	Bran	5
		100

Recipe No. 3

Week 1	Turkey starter crumbs fed *ad lib*
Week 2	Broiler pellets fed *ad lib* in food hoppers.
Onwards	Wet mash fed mid-day and evenings; e.g. boiled potatoes and scraps mixed with layers' mash to a crumbly consistency.

147

TWELVE WEEKS OLD THE DEAD LINE

Ducklings have to be fattened quickly and efficiently in a manner which enables maximum weight to be achieved at around nine weeks of age. Beyond twelve weeks the ducklings start to moult and lose weight. Replacing the body feathers involves extra feeding which is, of course, an additional cost.

There is also the problem of removing stubs from a duckling which starts to moult. This is a very tiresome business and may spoil the look of the carcass.

Except when *ad lib* feeding is practiced (e.g. pellets or crumbs constantly before the birds) regular feeding is essential. Some advocate an adequate feed of mash placed in troughs for the ducklings to eat within fifteen minutes and then removed. *Fresh* food is then given two hours later and so on.

At six weeks or age more food should be given. The addition of protein in the form of fish meal or meat and bone meal is essential. Exercise should be limited and so swimming water should not be provided. The aim is to induce the ducklings to eat as much as possible; therefore, a keen appetite is essential – usual in ducklings which are healthy and strong.

Remember a plentiful supply of good quality food is essential. Do not overfeed, but give the amount which increases body weight rapidly for quick maturity.

ESSENTIAL EQUIPMENT

The basic equipment required is as follows:
1. Food hoppers.
2. Water fountains or containers.

3. Bucket(s) for mixing.
4. A wooden spoon and/or small shovel for mixing mashes.
5. Wheelbarrow for carrying the mash (necessary when feeding large quantities).
6. Food troughs and hoppers.

Remember that cleanliness is essential so regular washing of equipment is desirable. Accordingly, galvanised or plastic utensils are probably best. Readers who wish to make their own appliances are advised to study *Poultry Houses and Appliances – A D.I.Y. Guide*

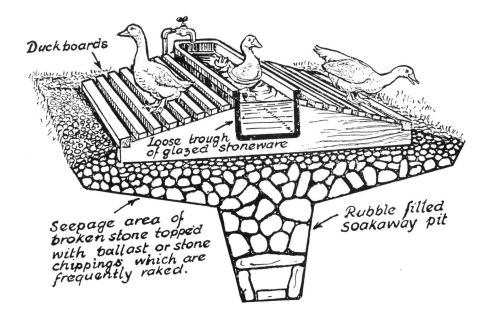

Duckboards

Loose trough of glazed stoneware

Seepage area of broken stone topped with ballast or stone chippings which are frequently raked.

Rubble filled soakaway pit

Chapter 18

THE GOOSE IN FABLE

SOCIAL CREATURES

Geese have existed for centuries. Around them has grown a great number of legends, superstitions and beliefs. They have inspired story tellers and poets who have chronicled their merits and lauded their mystique and special qualities.

GEESE AS PETS

Geese have been kept as pets or for special purposes. The Egyptians were said to be the first to use them as companions in the same way as cats. They were also kept for amusement by the Russians who gave ganders special training for goose fighting along the lines of the ancient sport of cockfighting, which was a national sport in Britain until around 1840 when it was made illegal.* This sport still exists in many countries and involves great skill in breeding and management. However, *goose fighting*, which may also have been practised in Britain, now appears to be a thing of the past.

Geese have been adopted as emblems or mascots. That

---
* Readers who wish to read further on this fascinating part of history are referred to *History of Cockfighting*, G.R. Scott, or *Cockfighting and Game Fowl*, H. Atkinson

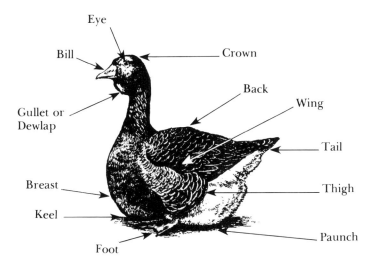

Figure 18.1   Points of a Goose
Tilly, a champion goose, bred by Mrs. Barbara Soames

famous regiment The Coldstream Guards adopted a gander, "Guardsman Jacob", and after he died his stuffed head
was kept in Wellington Barracks.

GOOSE DRIVES

In earlier times it was quite common for thousands of geese
to be driven from Norfolk, Suffolk, Lincolnshire and other
counties. Following harvest time the geese would be fed on
the corn stubble and once fat would then be driven at the
rate of about 8 miles per day. The boys controlling them
would drive them slowly along the road. Any geese becoming lame or ill would be collected up and put into a hospital
cart.

During the journey the geese would be fed regularly on
oats or barley. If not sustained in this way they would
obviously lose their plumpness.

151

GOOSE FAIRS

Goose fairs have been recorded over many centuries. Possibly the most common was the Michaelmas Goose Fair. Many reasons have been given for the Michaelmas day celebrations, but Harrison Weir (*Our Poultry*) suggests that the origin is probably based on a practical consideration; namely, that geese were then quite fat from the "stubble" feeding after the harvest is finished.

GEESE IN LEGEND

The legends relating to geese are numerous and carry great appeal. The goose which laid golden eggs is one of the best known fables.

Even children learn the legend of the goose by the words "Goosey, Goosey Gander ...".

Harrison Weir (ibid) compiled an enormous list of proverbs and sayings relating to geese; these are reproduced below:

OF GEESE

As deep drinketh the goose as the gander. — Howell, 1659. As one is, so the other.

As dizzy as a goose. — This is dazy or silly as a goose.

As is the gander so is the goose. — See foregoing.

By fits and starts, and girds as an ague, so takes a goose. — This is an allusion to its mode of feeding.

By little and little the fox eateth the goose. — Western. Many pickings, much meat.

A fat goose basteth itself. — That which good is, requires no help to make it better.

Every man basteth his fat goose. — He pays for who feeds it.

There's no goose so grey on the lake. — Gascoigne's "Posies," 1575.

They cannot find a gander for her mate (mete). — For every Jack there is a Jill.

Three women and a goose make a market. — This is enough to bargain about.

152

As good as goose skins that never man had enough. — Here the supposition is that the birds are inside their skins.

Before St. Chad every goose lays, both good and bad. — This but gives the natural time that eggs may be expected.

Children to bed and the goose to the fire. — Care and anxiety gone, then for peace and plenty.

Child's gosling, mother's goose. — This is so with children's pets, chickens, goslings or lambs, the child tends, the parent keeps.

Full of fun and gooster, like Mooney's goose. — Meaning unknown.

He can say Shoo! to a goose. — This is the opposite to the one, silly, simple, and frightened, that he cannot say Bo! to a goose.

Go shoe the goose. — You be doing something.

Shoeing the goose. — In the parish church of Whalley, Lancashire. It occurs under the seat of one of the stalls in the chancel and is supposed to be the abbot's stall. In the old Abbey of Whalley there is an inscription beneath it as follows:

"Whoso melles of wat men dos,
Let hym come hier and shoe the ghos."

A writer has rendered the inscription there as he thought to the spirit of the original —

"This fool to shoe a goose should try,
Who pokes his nose in each man's pie."

The more geese the more lovers. — In this is a covert sarcasm on the silliness of lovers. But the French newspaper *L'Europe*, December, 1865, gives another, shall I say, French version, as to the meaning:—

"It is customary in England for every gentleman admitted into society to send a fat goose at Christmas to the lady of the house he is in the habit of visiting (?) — the beautiful receive a whole magazine — and are thus enabled to tell the number of their lovers by the number of the geese sent to them." — *The Times*, December 27th, 1865. Comment is needless.

You find fault with a fat goose. — You are not satisfied with the best.

Young is the goose that will eat no oats. — Lyly's "Euphues," 1580; re-print, 1868, page 366.

A goose is a goose. — Sussex and Kent. A thing is what it is, not what too often it is represented to be.

What is sauce for the gander is sauce for the goose, or, What is sauce for the goose is sauce for the gander. — Ray's "Notes": "This is a woman's proverb."

Tittle, tattle! give the goose more hay. — Food keeps most things quiet.

When the fox is full he hateth geese. — None cares if there is no want.

We desire but one feather from your goose. — Let me have a finger in the pie.

He hopes to see a goose graze on your head. — That is, eat the grass on your grave. He wishes you dead.

He sets the fox to keep his geese. — Dy Res's "English Proverbs," 1709. He who would not lose set not a rogue to watch.

He stole a goose and stuck down a feather. — Heywood, 1562.* He would make believe a fox had taken it.

He that eats the king's geese will be choked with the feathers. — He is sure to suffer sooner or later.

> *He that will in East Cheap, eat a goose so fat,*
> *With harp, pipe, and song,*
> *He must sleep in Newgate on a mat,*
> *Be the night never so long.* — Old Song. This of the

spendthrift.

> *He who will have a full flock*
> *Must have an old steg (gander) and a young cock.* — Lancashire. He

that follows Nature's laws fares best.

> *England were but a fling,*
> *Save for the crooked stick, and the grey goose wing.* — That is, England

would have been a lost land, or not tenable, were it not for the bow and arrows. This was the saying in praise of archery. Grose's "Provincial Glossary," 1787.

A fox should not be on the jury when a goose is tried. — No one gets justice when the judge is biassed.

A goose cannot graze after him. — As a goose grazes closer than anything, this means he takes all, he leaves nothing.

A goose quill gentleman. — This was said of lawyers, who often carried their pen stuck behing their ear when at their office.

A goose-quill is more dangerous than a lion's claw. — Oft by writing does more lasting injury.

A wild goose never laid a tame egg. — As the father and mother so the child.

A young wife and a harvest goose, much cackle with both. — A harvest goose is a goose at its best, young and lively.

All his geese are swans, and he never had ducks. — Sussex and Kent, etc. He is too big for small things.

---

* "Recompensyng former loytryng lyfe loose,
As did the pure penytent that stole a goose
And stuck down a feather."

Figure 18.2   Geese for the Christmas Market, 1885

155

As big as a goose egg. — "Pierce the Ploughman's Creed" (A.D. 1394), Skeat's ed., line 225. This is a natural measurement.

Green-goose fair. — In "Wily Beguiled," 1606. "Go to green-goose fair." Country fairs were said to be kept by foxes for the catching of geese.

Greenwich geese. — Greenwich pensioners. A poor or old sailor.

A goose without mustard is better than no goose. — Kent and Sussex. Half a loaf is better than no bread.

He wags his head like a goose, though as wise as an owl. — He pretends to be simple to catch the unwary.

If she be a goose, her dame well to pay,
She'll lay two eggs ere Valentine's Day. — A hen-wife's truism.

March goslings. — Sussex. Wild impudent fellows.

March birds are best. — Things in proper season thrive.

When a goose dances, and a fowl versifies, there is sport. — Each are ludicrous.

If there is ice that will bear a duck before Martinmass, there'll be none that'll bear a goose all the winter. — A very doubtful omen.

It is a blind goose that knows not a fox from a fern bush. — An enemy is seldom mistaken for that which he is not.

It is a silly goose that comes to a fox's sermon. — He speaks fair who would catch the fool.

A goose is a poor thing, too much for one, not enough for two. — Sussex and Kent. This phrase is attributed to Queen Elizabeth, but is a common saying in Kent and Sussex.

It is as much pity to see a woman weep as a goose to go barefoot. — One is as easy to do as the other. Withal's "Dictionary," ed. 1634.

Like a syringe to a Hampshire goose. — Guilpin's "Skialetheia," 1598. Both enticing.

Set the hare's head against the goose's giblets. — As value against value.

Shall the goslings teach the goose to swim or the gander to gaggle. — See similar proverb.

I have a goose to pluck with you. — Howell's "Proverbs," 1659. This was originally "a crow to pluck with you." In heiroglyphics a crow symbolises "contention." Thus two plucking at one would doubtless settle the quarrel, if any.

All his swans are geese. — All his boasted expectations have ended in nothing. He sees more than there is.

All his geese are swans. — Is another and reverse rendering. This is when a man sees what he possesses with a biassed vision. In other words, exaggerates and magnifies with the intention of deceiving others, and so is sometimes himself unwittingly deceived.

The goslings would lead the geese to grass. — French. The young would teach the old.

To pluck the goose without making it cry out. — French. Is to rob little by little, so that the loss is not seen or felt.

A quiet goose eats the most food. — Southern. He eats much that talks little.

Every goose after her kind. — Kent and Sussex. Birds of a feather flock together.

Gone is the goose that the great egg did lay. — Killed is the goose that laid the golden egg. What is profitable, keep.

Good geese don't bite. — This does not explain itself.

Good meat men may pick from a goose's eye. — Taylor's "Goose," 1621.

A fat goose and a sure sale. — A good article, a ready market.

Goose, gander, and goslings, are three sounds, but one thing. — This is obvious.

Goslings lead the geese to water. — The young go, the old follow.

When the rain raineth, and the goose winketh, little wots the gosling what the goose thinketh. — Skelton's "Garlande of Laurell," 1523.

Geese can be plucked as long as they have feathers. — You can cheat people of their goods as long as they have any.

If all fools wore white caps, we should see a flock of geese. — None would go bare-headed.

Geese with geese, and women with women. — Like and like agree.

The older the goose the harder to pluck. — More life more cunning.

I'll cook your goose. — Common town slang. By some thought to be, "I'll have what you have and use it."

Go cry Bo! to a goose. — May not a fool cry Bo! to a goose, or the contrarie. Armiers's "Italian and his Boy," 1609

Where there are women and geese there wants no gaggling. — Much talk, and both in their way.

One goose will not stock a common. — Sussex. This was said of one taking land with little money.

Two geese and a gander will pay the rent. — Sussex. This in derision of one with a small farm.

PRACTICAL QUALITIES

The liver of the goose – usually the Embden goose is fattened to the point where the liver is greatly enlarged and
then after killing the goose the paté is made. It is rich and
strong.

A recipe from an old cookery book is as follows:

Paté de Foie Gras

2 lb goose liver	2 tablespoons water
8 oz lard	3 tablespoons port wine
pinch ground cloves	salt and black pepper
½ bay leaf	flour and water paste
1 dessertspoon chopped parsley	

Chop liver and fry gently in lard until brown. Mince and mix
with cloves, parsley, salt and black pepper. Moisten with the
wine and water which should be just enough to hold the
mixture together. Place in terrine and press down firmly.
Place terrine in dish of water. Cover paté with thin layer of
lard – stick bay leaf on top. Seal edges with flour and water
paste. Place in fairly hot oven and cook for 3½ hours. Serve
cold.

Above all the goose can supply all these things with little
or no special attention. It is said that geese will thrive where
no other grazers would have sufficient food. Moreover,
they will improve rough pasture, eliminating weeds and
improving the growth of grass by the natural manuring of
the land. This applies particularly when an area can be
rested for a few months between running geese on the
pasture.

Chapter 19

MANAGEMENT OF GEESE

THE "SET"

Geese put together for breeding purposes are usually referred to as a "set". The gander is placed with a number of geese. Some writers recommend not more than two geese, but others suggest as many as five being a suitable number. Much depends on the virility of the gander and existing conditions, but certainly if too many are included in the set the eggs may not be fertile. With the very large geese it is certainly advisable to limit the number of females.

The birds should be placed together in the autumn and, if possible, the arrangement should last the whole season. There is nothing more disturbing to the geese than being introduced to new companions. When placed in the run the geese should be locked in a suitable fox-proof shed for a few days. This then enables them to associate the accomodation with "home" into which they can be driven each night. After a period they will probably go into the shed by themselves.

Geese mature slowly and live for a considerable period – 20 years or even longer. However, because of this slow development, geese should not be bred from until they are at least 2 years of age. Indeed, with a gander, maturity may

159

not be reached until he is 3-4 years of age. Goslings from young parents may turn out to be rather weak.

Once a set is breeding, success may be achieved for a long period often exceeding 10 years.

ACCOMMODATION

Geese will thrive in any type of accommodation built along the lines suggested for ducks. Each goose should have floor space of around 4 square feet. Floor litter of leaves or shavings should be changed regularly or the floor will become wet and unhygienic.

Ventilation is absolutely vital and, therefore, wire netting or slats should be provided to allow a constant flow of air.

Nest boxes may be provided — one per goose — and these should be around 2 feet 6 inches square. Fresh straw should be placed in each nest box. However, keep a watchful eye on any likely quiet spots where a goose may lay. All eggs should be collected daily and, if the goose is to be allowed to sit, pot eggs should be put into the nest. A goose may become broody after 30 eggs have been laid.

In the breeding season a food hopper may be kept in the shed containing layers' pellets. This will supplement the normal food giving the proteins essential for successful breeding.

THE RUN

Geese may be kept in a limited run, but this is not advisable. They are large birds which feed primarily on grass. Accordingly, around ½ acre of grazing land is essential and with a set of 4-5 geese an area of 2-3 acres is advisable. Otherwise,

Exhibition-Type Embden Gander

Top: White Chinese Geese
Bottom: Sebastopol Geese

Toulouse Geese

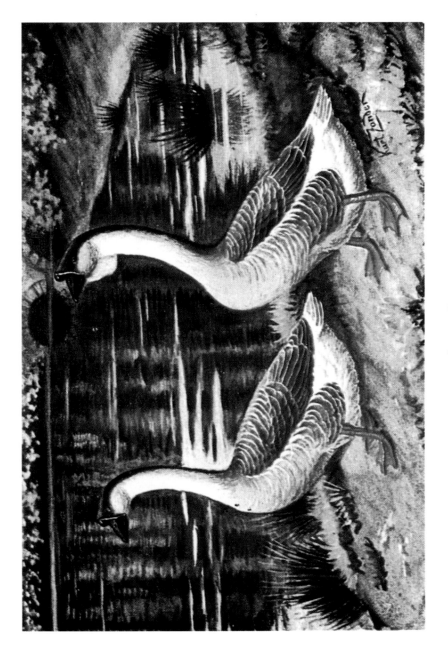

African Geese

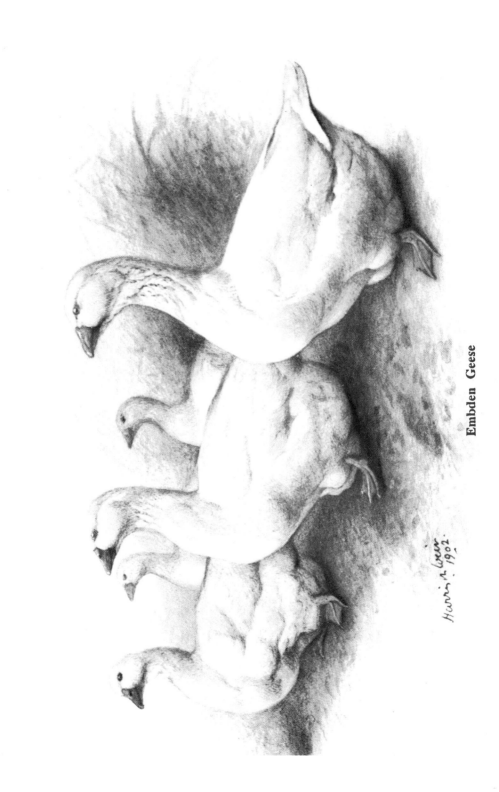

Embden Geese

Harri. N. Lever
1902.

Pomeranian Gander

This is grey and white, but other colours exist; they are popular in Germany.

BRECON BUFF

CHINESE

EMBDEN

ROMAN

SEBASTOPOL

TOULOUSE

Charles Francis

A Comparative Line-Up of Geese

FRANCES FRY

Ornamental–Type Geese
For details see *Fancy Waterfowl* , F Finn.

1. Chinese Goose
2. Canada Goose
3. Red-Breasted Goose
4. Magellan Goose ♀ & ♂
5. Barnacle Goose
6. Egyptian Goose
7. Emperor Goose
8. Maned Goose
   (or Australian Wood Duck)

Figure 19.1   A set of White Chinese Geese

(*Photo courtesy:* Anita-Dawn Allen)

161

particularly early in the season, the area will not yield sufficient food.

The area of the run should be surrounded by wire netting. If it is to be fox-proof then wire at least 6 feet high is
essential. Furthermore, wire should be laid on the ground
on the outside of the fence, thus preventing a fox from
scratching a hole and going underneath.

Within the run there should be a pond, or, at least, a
suitable water fountain. **Adequate fresh water is vital.** This
need not be swimming water although it is thought that the
presence of a pond does improve fertility.

BREEDING SEASON

Geese should commence laying in February, but the precise
date depends on age of the birds, weather, food available
and related factors. Some start earlier and others later.

Once started a goose will lay a clutch of eggs – usually
between 12 and 30 eggs. As noted earlier each egg should
be collected daily and replaced by a pot egg. Then once the
goose becomes seriously broody — becoming aggressive,
hissing and staying on the nest constantly – the proper eggs
may be put under her.

As with any broody, she should be segregated from the
rest, being placed in a small shed or coop. The goose should
be allowed off the nest daily and given food and water. She
may be allowed to run in the same area as the other geese,
thus remaining as part of the set.

A broody hen may also be used for hatching. However,
whereas a goose will cover around 15 eggs, a broody hen
will probably cover between 4 and 6 eggs. This means that
quite a number of broodies will be required and for this

reason an incubator may be employed.

Although difficulty used to be experienced with artificial incubation of goose eggs, modern methods enable them to be hatched quite successfully. The incubation period is around 30 days with a possible time of 28-30 days, (but possibly as long as 34 days). The hatching procedure is similar to that for ducks.

If the maximum number of eggs is to be obtained then a goose should not be allowed to sit on her eggs. She can then be induced to lay more eggs within the laying period which covers from early in the year to July. Once this period has elapsed no more eggs will be laid and the season is over. The total number of eggs laid will depend very much on the breed and the food supplied. Around 30 eggs is normal, but some geese will lay more than 60; the good layers may exceed 100 eggs.

GRAZING

There must be ample grass for the geese to graze. In winter supply them with pellets or, when the water is not frozen, wheat soaked in water is quite beneficial.

They may be allowed to roam around an orchard or even a semi-woodland enclosure. However, do remember that they may damage young trees and certain trees and plants are not good for them. Usually, if a tree is poisonous; e.g. Laburnum, then it is better to fence it off.

Geese are tremendous foragers and will, therefore, keep an area quite clean and the grass quite short. With a large enough area they will fend for themselves. If there is inadequate food to be found a goose will "go light" and may even die. For this reason sound management is absolutely essential. Moreover, the fancier or breeder should watch very carefully for any signs of geese losing weight or looking rather lifeless.

If in doubt, and always when birds are laying or being fattened, keep a hopper well topped-up with layers' pellets. This should be kept indoors or the food will spoil; moreover, wild birds and other creatures will consume a tremendous amount of food. This is too expensive to waste!

Green stuff such as kale and cabbage may also be given. Some farmers also feed root crops such as turnips which are finely minced. **Remember though, that grass should be the main food; it is cheap and effective.**

HOME MADE RATIONS FOR GEESE

As noted earlier, goslings and adult geese will forage for themselves and, therefore, a great deal of food will be obtained from the pasture being used. The fact remains that goslings *must* have extra food with a high protein content at the early stages and the adults should be given extra food when laying or being fattened. This may be in the form of manufactured goods or home made rations which, though time consuming, will tend to be cheaper.

Possible recipes are given below:

1. *Goslings*

As an alternative to turkey starter crumbs and growers' pellets purchased from a feed mill, the following may be mixed and fed:

(a)   **1 Day to 8 Weeks**

	Parts
Barley Meal	2
Ground Oats	1
Weatings	5
Bran	1
Meat and Bone Meal	$\frac{1}{2}$
Linseed Meal (or Cod Liver)	$\frac{1}{2}$

This should be mixed with water to a crumbly state and fed 5 times per day.

(b)   **8 Weeks Onwards (Stock birds)**

	Parts
Barley Meal or Maize Meal	3
Weatings	4
Bran	1
Meat and Bone Meal	$\frac{1}{2}$

Again, this should be fed as a crumbly, wet mash but only once per day, early in the morning. The evening meal should be corn soaked in water.

(c)   **8 Weeks Onwards (Table birds)**

	Parts
Barley Meal or Maize Meal	3
Weatings	4
Small Potatoes (cooked)	4
Bran	1
Meat and Bone Meal	$\frac{1}{2}$

This should be given as a crumbly, wet mash in the mornings and soaked corn should be given in the evenings.

165

2. *Adult Geese (Laying)*

	Parts
Ground Oats	2
Maize Meal	1
Weatings	4
Bran	1
Meat and Bone Meal	1

This, fed as a wet mash, should be given in the mornings and soaked grain in the evenings.

Further requirements

With geese it is essential to observe the following:

(a) With wet mash, remove after about 20 minutes or the food will go sour and the geese will lose their appetites.

(b) Try to gauge the correct amount they will eat to fill their crops to capacity without excessive waste.

(c) Make sure there is adequate grit available (soluble and insoluble) and water at all times.

INCUBATION

If **natural** incubation is to be employed then the broody hen, goose or turkey should be placed in a suitable coop or shed. The following points should be observed:

1. Make a definite basin shape in the earth floor of the coop. This keeps the large eggs in position.

2. Damp earth should be used on top of a wire floor. This should be lined with straw or hay.

The broody hen should be closed up and let out for a short period each day. With the broody goose it may not be wise to have a door on the coop – a goose cannot be lifted off the nest very easily. Accordingly, provided the goose cannot be attacked by predators she will take care of her own chores, coming off each day for food and water and then going back.

Young goslings take quite a time to emerge from the eggs. They are slow workers and may take many hours to hatch after the eggs have "pipped".

Breeders of geese usually recommend that eggs placed under a broody hen should be turned twice a day. This is presumably a safety measure – the hen normally turns eggs herself, but with eggs the size of a goose egg there is certainly a physical problem.

With *artificial* incubation the appropriate level of humidity is vital. This means keeping the moisture trays full and ensuring there is adequate ventilation.

REARING GOSLINGS

Goslings may be reared by the goose, by a broody hen or by the use of an infra-red lamp or other artificial method of rearing. Ideally, the goslings should be allowed to graze in specially prepared runs which have wire-netting at the top, round the sides and *underneath*. The latter is essential to prevent predators digging underneath and taking the young.

During the first few weeks, turkey starter crumbs may be fed and a drinking trough should be kept filled with water so the goslings can immerse their heads. The run should be moved daily, thus allowing the goslings to systematically eat the grass.

At about 2 weeks old the brood can be allowed to run in an orchard or paddock to fend for themselves. However,

Figure 19.2 Chinese Geese with Young (This pair are rather too horizontal in carriage for pure Chinese).

growers' pellets should now be given, being placed in a gravity-feed hopper inside a shed where the young geese are driven each evening. Remember that rapid growth is essential!

Adult feeding can commence at 3 months of age. This can include wheat or maize soaked in water and mixed with growers' mash. After a few days the corn can be fed by itself. A quantity of around 2-4 oz (56.70-113.40 g) per bird will bring them on extremely well. Watch carefully to make sure that this supplementary food is eaten up fiarly quickly. Soaking corn in water makes it more palatable and, of course, keeps it away from land birds and rats.

As noted, precautions against foxes, rats, crows and other predators is vital in the early stages. In the coop a strong floor is essential and, as noted earlier, the floor of the run should be covered with strong wire netting. Special care of the goslings in the early days will pay dividends. Keep them dry and specially protected for the first 7 days.

Geese were once very popular for feasts and were fattened for either Michaelmas (29th September) or Christmas. The former festival lost its importance and, with the growing popularity of the turkey, the goose lost its place in the gastronomic world. Indeed, for quite a period it seemed that the goose had disappeared from the culinary scene altogether.

Never underestimate the changes in taste! For Christmas the goose is once more in demand. Fed on grass, the old fashioned flavour is still obtainable to be enjoyed by those who appreciate something different. The turkey is now another accepted "package" which mass production methods have not improved. This is probably the reason for the new interest in the goose.

169

Figure 20.1   Standard Type of Embden Goose

170

Chapter 20

EMBDEN GEESE

ORIGIN

According to records, the Embden goose is a relative new-comer being in existence for less than 200 years. Originally the birds were imported from the continent, either from Holland or Germany or possibly both. The eminent author-ity, Lewis Wright, was of the opinion that they came from Embden, Westphalia. Edward Brown, in *Races of Domestic Poultry*, believed that the Embden was created by crossing the German White with the English White and then, by careful selection, creating the goose known today.

Some writers have suggested that the great size obtained in the English Embden is due to a cross with the Toulouse which has then been "bred out", but still retaining the larger size. A cross which has recently occurred will certainly show itself, for the Toulouse has a distinct gullet and is "soft feathered". The Embden, on the other hand, is noted for the *hardness of feather*; i.e. tight feathers closely encasing the body.

DESCRIPTION

The Embden goose is a hardy bird; a good forager which

grows quickly and reaches a weight of around 20 lb for the goose and 30 lb for the gander. These should be regarded as minimum sizes, 10 % above being quite usual in good specimens.

In colour the Embden should be *pure white*. Bill, shanks and feet should be orange, with the short bill being of a lighter shade. The legs should be "fairly short", (*British Poultry Standards*), but in practice they are much longer than the Toulouse and possibly "*medium legs*" would be a more appropriate description. They should appear strong enough to carry the great weight and, obviously, the toes should be webbed.

The *head* should be reasonably long and oval shaped on a long and graceful neck without any sign of the gullet or dewlap found on the Toulouse. The eyes are blue.

In body there should be considerable bulk, well-rounded in shape, with a long back and medium sized tail. The breast should be rounded, but with a certain amount of "cut away" towards the legs. There should be no pronounced keel. The wings should be very strong and of reasonable length.

UTILITY PROPERTIES

Generally an adult Embden will commence laying fairly early – possibly in February. It may lay in the region of 30-40 eggs. Since this goose tends to come broody, there will probably be time for two sittings only. However, she may be "broken off" to resume laying as soon as possible.

As a meat producer the Embden is regarded as being excellent. The goslings should be ready for killing at 5-6 months and, when fed with a high protein food, possibly even earlier. The white feathers make the flesh more attractive than those with dark plumage.

172

Beak too
narrow
and dark

Gullet

Dark feathers
on wings and
tail

Paunch not
deep enough

Legs too short and
dark

Figure 20.2 Embden with faults

173

The great size is an advantage and yet a deterrent, for who wishes to have a 30 lb goose in the oven except, of course, at Christmas. However, for commercial establishments such as hotels, the Embden should be a good proposition.

EXHIBITION REQUIREMENTS

The exhibition requirements are outlined above. A goose is very much a utility bird and should be judged as such. Essentials are as follows:

1. Large body which is positively long and has an upright carriage.
2. Oval head with no signs of coarseness.
3. Gracefulness of neck.
4. Strong legs.
5. Correct colour in plumage, eyes, bill and shanks.

Features which are quite clearly in opposition to these requirements should be penalised. Any signs of crossing with the Toulouse – grey features or gullet – should be regarded as major faults.

Chapter 21

TOULOUSE GEESE*

ORIGIN

The breed itself is a very old one; known by the name from 1555. They originated in the area around Toulouse as grey geese, being almost identical to the Greylag in colouring and markings, but of heavier build.

They caught the attention of Lord Derby in 1840, and he imported some to England. From that point onwards the French Toulouse were used as breeding stock for English breeders and by 1894 we had produced massive birds of over 30 lb in weight. The winner of the 1894 National Poultry Show award for geese was a Toulouse gander of 34 lb in weight! In America ganders have been recorded of 40 lb, but today the poultry *standards* might expect ganders to weigh 26-28 lb with the goose from 20-22 lb at adulthood.

The Toulouse in France has never quite equalled such weights, although many more are still kept in that country than here in England.

Their trusting, placid temperaments do not lend themselves to being kept in very large flocks of mixed breeds if

* Chapter based on material supplied by Mrs. Barbara Soames.

they are to do really well. The more active jostling and aggression of large numbers of other breeds distresses them, putting them off mating and sometimes resulting in their being unable to get their fair share of food at the trough. They are very "domestic" geese and are confused by the more agile habits of others. If included in a breeding flock in equal numbers to Embdens they are better suited than when in a minority. They do not need a pond for successful mating; indeed, some Toulouse will never mate in the water. They rarely have difficulty in producing fertile eggs in spite of rumour to the contrary. The only times fertility may be low is when the weather has been very severe through winter and spring – and at such times most breeds of geese suffer from low fertility also.

Toulouse are by far the most popular breed of geese in most of the U.S.A., where Buff Toulouse have been bred in recent years. In France, from whence they came originally, the Toulouse "agricole" is a reminder of what the original stock that was imported by Lord Derby may have looked like. However, even in France, carefully selective breeding has brought some large flocks to as good a standard as we have in this country.

DESCRIPTION

Toulouse should give the impression of plumpness, with a large "oblong" shape when viewed from the side.

The stomach (or paunch) should be even-sided and touching the ground between the legs. The keel (or bow) should be as full as possible to the front; in the very best specimens, near to touching the ground.

An absence of any keel is a defect leading to disqualification when showing, and such birds should not be

176

Figure 21.1 Katie and Tess – Toulouse Geese at 9 months of age
(Bred by Mrs. Barbara Soames. *Photo courtesy:* Focus Photography)

included in a breeding plan. It is the most difficult feature to attain and the inclusion of poorly-keeled stock for breeding will increase the possibilities of further similar stock in the future.

Toulouse must always have a gullet (or pouch) under the lower beak. It should be large and convoluted. The head should be large, and specimen birds with small narrow heads should be discarded. The cheeks become rather "jowly" with increasing age; this is quite permissible.

The neck should be thick in appearance, carried in a vertical position, with very little curvature. The back should be broad, almost horizontal, from the back of the neck up to the tail, where the line of the back rises up to meet the tail feathers in a sudden tip.

Birds with a down-turn of back at the tail should be avoided. The wings are very large and should cross over neatly near the tail. The legs are of medium length, but in a good specimen appear to be short, as the thigh coverts cover most of them.

The plumage is soft, and fairly loose feathered, especially on the paunch. This loose feathering is even noticeable in baby goslings, whose down is longer and fluffier than that of any other goose except the Sebastopol.

Because good Toulouse are very big, the general carriage is slow, dignified and stately.

Feather colours are as follows: apart from a white paunch the rest of the bird is in tones of grey. The lightest grey is found on the keel and up to the dewlap; the darker grey (a soft dark grey) on the back and wings. There is often a slightly darker feathering from the back of the head running down to the back. The tail is mainly grey, but with a prominent white band across the end of the feathers. All the dark grey feathers are edged with a very pale grey except for the primary or flight feathers, which are almost black.

The breast shades from light grey at the bow of the chest, to white as the bow and keel join the paunch.

The legs and feet should be orangey-pink; in babies the legs, feet and beak are nearly black, but this gradually grows paler until an ever-deepening pink finally changes to an orange tone. Often a dark bean on the end of the beak is present until almost a year old in females, when this colour also changes to the required adult white.

Eyes are hazel to dark brown, alert, but not too aggressive an appearance.

Lastly, as regards plumage, in strong sunlight and with age, Toulouse often develop a brownish tinge on many of the black feathers. This is allowable and their new plumage grows back to the correct soft grey when the summer comes round again.

CHARACTERISTICS

There is no doubt that breeding really good quality exhibition Toulouse is a challenge to the owner.

It is very difficult to get both a broad back and a deep keel, together with overall size. The Toulouse breeder probably eyes his or her young goslings more closely than for any other breed. There is so much to hope for in order to rear that "perfect" bird, and there is an enormous thrill to actually breeding and rearing a truly large and magnificent specimen.

The careful observation of the baby flock will have to go on for at least 9 months, as some Toulouse are very slow developers. To discard too early may well be a mistake, as I have known it take until that age for a good keel and gullet to form. However, I would also say that, in my experience, if birds have not developed a good keel by this age, they rarely do so as they get older. The gullet does grow with advancing years, *but* only if there is one there at about 9 months of age.

In general, though, by 4 months old, most of the baby goslings will be shaping up sufficiently to give their owner some rough idea of what standard of adulthood they will probably attain. For example, two or so goslings out of a dozen will be undersized and probably with little keel and can be culled at 4 months or so. What are worth hanging on to for much longer are those large goslings; they may turn into champions soon.

A paunch is the first feature to develop, often dropping below "knee" level at 8 weeks or so; it seems an easy-to-acquire piece of their anatomy. The broadening of the back is also apparent by this age, the gullet and the keel forming later on.

One thing is very certain in Toulouse rearing; they must have access to *ad lib* nutritious food in their first three months. They are, on average, smaller goslings (4 oz) on hatching than the Embden, from eggs little bigger than those of Chinese. From that point they need feeding really well if they are to do their owners credit later on. Plenty of additional calcium (such as limestone granules) should be fed in a separate dish, as a good big frame needs to be built.

If good grass is available the owner will not be bank-rupted over their bought feed – but it is not sufficient for Toulouse to begin with. They will appear to prefer grass, but will ingest both feed and grass in equal proportions if available. To economise when Toulouse are young is

180

Gullet too
small

Breast not full
enough

Keel and paunch
should be nearer
the ground and
more full and
rounded

Figure 21.2 Toulouse Goose of Utility type showing faults

short-sighted for, once the first few months are over, the young growing birds seem to gradually eat less and less, until in full adulthood they eat considerably smaller quantities of feed than Embdens or cross-breds.

UTILITY PROPERTIES

The Toulouse is a much better layer than the Embden; some strains almost equal the best of any goose breed. My four year old goose, Martha, laid 109 eggs last year, and surprised everyone by becoming broody at the end of the year and successfully rearing goslings. Toulouse are generally not good sitters, but if you can arrange matters so that everything goes smoothly with nothing to worry the sitter, once they have been broody, my experience is that they will do so every year.

However, this sitting instinct seems to have been bred out of them to some extent, and they are easily persuaded to give up, if you would rather keep the goose laying.

Some strains are less productive, laying around 50 eggs per season; young females rarely lay more than this in their first two seasons.

This laying ability of the breed has been a reason for using a Toulouse female to mate with an Embden male. Embden females are not so prolific, and so more goslings are acquired by crossing. The other reason for crossing, is that the Toulouse ganders tend to be slow to mature, often not managing to fertilise many eggs – or even trying to – until their second season. The Toulouse goose however, is able and willing to mate at about 10 months of age, and so also are Embden males.

From a production point of view, the Embden ×

Toulouse makes very good sense, especially as the cross-bred goslings frequently hatch better, are more vigorous, and make quicker weight gains in the first 7 months. After that point of time, the growth of Embden × Toulouse goslings falls off very rapidly, whereas Toulouse go on steadily gaining. For the Michaelmas goose trade in particular, an "early gain" Embden × Toulouse goose is ideal. Where Toulouse have such an important part to play, genetically speaking, is in their ability to convert food to weight easily. Should the breed die out, it would be difficult to maintain the overall size of cross-bred geese, needing longer periods of penning prior to Christmas, thus costing more to produce the table bird.

For the person who intends to keep a pair or a trio of Toulouse, and rear younsters for sale or for eating, there are three important points. Firstly, the breed is far less aggressive than all other breeds, apart from the Sebastopol; they are not wanderers, preferring to stay near the house and its owners. This makes them ideally suited to a small acreage; an orchard perhaps, or large garden.

Secondly, they provide more interest to the breeder, as explained previously, with additional pride and pleasure in owning some "good" ones.

Thirdly, there is always a ready sale for one's goslings for adding to breeding stock; they are, sadly, not so widely kept in England as previously, yet the demand is there. Those birds which are not up to standard may be sold and despatched for the table; they make tender and delicious eating without fattening.

Figure 22.1　A Pair of White Chinese Geese

Chapter 22

CHINESE GEESE

BRIEF HISTORY

As the name suggests, these geese originated from China, where they were domesticated centuries ago, being of very ancient origin.

When they arrived in the United Kingdom is not clear, but evidence available suggests around 1850 (E.S. Dixon, a Victorian writer), but it seems that geese complying with the Chinese description have been in existence in Europe for many centuries. The breed went under many names such as China Goose, Swan Goose, Knob Goose, Robin Goose and Siberian Goose.

The famous naturalist Frederick Cuvier classified the Chinese Goose as a swan, naming it *Cygnus Auseroides*, but it was later re-classified as a goose having the sixteen cervical vertibrae of that species. The original mistake was understandable because the resemblance to a swan is quite positive.

DESCRIPTION

This goose is coloured *white* or *brown* and is classified under these two colours. The Brown is also know as the "Grey"

185

and in fact the colour is a mixture of brown, grey and white. In the White goose the bill, knob, shanks and toes are orange. With the Brown goose the knob and bill are dark slate with the shanks and toes orange. Eyes are blue in the White and brown in the Brown goose.

The shape of the body is oval with a well rounded breast and wings carried high. The carriage is upright and the neck is long thus giving the bird the appearance of a swan.

A feature of the head is the knob which is really an extension of the bill. It should be quite prominent, the male having the larger knob.

UTILITY FEATURES

Chinese geese weigh from 8 to 12 lb, the gander being heavier than the goose. They are, therefore, quite compact with a good distribution of flesh. This size suits the modern household more than does the giants; the Toulouse or Embden.

As layers they are extremely good performers. They commence laying early, often in the autumn and continue for around 6 months. The eggs are a whitish colour of medium size and around 40-50 eggs may be laid in a season.

EXHIBITION FAULTS

Chinese geese should comply as closely as possible to the *standard*. Typical points of departure which should be penalised are as follows:

    1. Inadequate or complete absence of knob.
    2. Wrong position of knob.
    3. Body faults such as:
      (a) oversize;

Figure 22.2   Standard type of Brown Chinese Goose

187

Small knob

Narrow beak

Evidence of gullet

Lack of upright carriage

Incorrect feather colour

Figure 22.3   Brown Chinese Goose showing faults

(b)   wrong shape;
(c)   low lying body;
(d)   too long;
(e)   roach back;
(f)   wings carried too low.
4. Neck lacking slender, graceful curve and appropriate length; e.g. thick straight neck.
5. Colour incorrect; e.g.
   (a)   In **Whites**, any other colour.
   (b)   In **Browns**, the wrong overall colour or white feathers in wings.

The knob is an important feature of this bird. This should be as large as possible, round in shape and quite erect. However, an allowance should be made for the age of a bird.

Oversized birds should also be penalised. Chinese should be graceful and, therefore, any tendency towards coarseness is a serious fault.

Some Chinese geese used to have a dewlap under the throat, but this is not apparent in modern specimens. It is still found in the African Goose described in Chapter 24.

Figure 23.1 Standard Type of Roman Goose

Chapter 23

ROMAN GEESE

ORIGIN

Roman geese originated in Italy and are of very ancient origin. They were kept in the city of Rome and were regarded as sacred to Juno (Goddess of Marriage). If these ancient geese are the same type of birds as found today then it can be established that the breed is more than 2,000 years old.

The ability of geese to act as watchdogs is well known. Roman geese are said to have given the alarm when Rome was attacked by the Gauls in the year 365 B.C.

In modern times small, white geese are to be found throughout Europe. They were thought to be a minor form of Embden (in terms of size), but subsequently they were regarded as being descended from Roman geese. The Roman goose is believed to have been introduced to England around 1903.

DESCRIPTION

The Roman goose is a relatively small bird reaching a weight of around 12 to 15 lb, the larger weight being the gander. In shape it is very similar to the Embden but, due to the weight difference, is much more compact.

The overall shape is made up of a broad body and a fully rounded breast which is fairly low. The wings should be quite strong and carried high up on the body. With the emphasis on lighter bones, the amount of flesh is relatively high.

Although the head is similar to the Embden the *standard* specifies that it should be "well rounded". The neck is of *medium* length, yet the Roman goose is quite graceful, each part of the body being in proportion with the remainder. The short bill should be orange-red and the legs and feet should be orange. Eyes are a light blue.

UTILITY PROPERTIES

In terms of usefulness, the Roman goose is said to excel in both laying and rapid flesh development. Roman geese have been known to lay more than 100 eggs per bird. Moreover, they may start laying at a fairly early age (e.g. 6 months). They can be used as broodies, but may be late in getting the urge. Accordingly, the early eggs should be hatched by incubator or broody hen.

For fattening ready for the table they put on flesh at a rapid rate. At 6 months of age they will probably achieve around 8 lb and at 9 months they will make up to as much as 14 lb.

EXHIBITION REQUIREMENTS

The Roman goose is primarily a utility bird and should be judged on that basis. The essential features are as shown below:

1. A compact plump body with close fitting feathers.

Black, instead of blue, eye

Misshapen head

Dark bill

Curved back

Dark feathers

Excessive paunch

Misshapen body — evidence of keel

AJW

Figure 23.2   Roman Goose with faults

193

2. The carriage should be horizontal.
3. Lightness of bone without any coarseness.
4. Correct size with tightly fitted feathers.
5. Correct colour of plumage (white), shanks, bill and eyes.

Any feature which is uncharacteristic of the breed should be penalised when being judged.

Figure 24.1   African Geese

(From Wright's *New Book of Poultry*)

Chapter 24

OTHER VARIETIES OF GEESE

The main breeds of domestic geese are covered in earlier chapters. Some other varieties are considered in this chapter.

AFRICAN GEESE

Although claims are made for this goose being quite distinct from the Chinese there are many who doubt this claim. Indeed, it would appear that the breed is a larger version of the Chinese weighing as much as 25 lb being, therefore, twice the size of its smaller cousin.

Edward Brown (*Races of Domestic Poultry*) suggests that the additional size may be the result of crossing the Chinese with the Toulouse. Certainly the existence of dewlap, found in this breed, appears to confirm the Toulouse blood.

Utility Features
The African goose is primarily a table bird. It lays only tolerably well, a figure of around 20 eggs per year being quoted as normal, although some strains may do better. Where it excels is in the development of flesh and obviously its claim to fame must be as a table bird.

Exhibition Requirements

The general appearance is that of the Chinese goose, but obviously it is much heavier and does not have the same gracefulness or elevated carriage.

The body is large and long with a straight back. In its carriage the African goose is fairly upright and there is no evidence of keel. The breast should be well rounded and prominent.

The head should be large and topped with a black knob. The neck should be stout and strong and slightly curved. A prominent dewlap is essential.

Short, powerful thighs and medium length shanks carry the heavy body with a reasonable amount of gracefulness.

Colours are Brown or White. In **Browns** there is a dark brown stripe stretching from the top of the head to the bottom of the neck. The remainder of the body is ash brown varying in shade from *light* on the head, neck and body to a darker colour on the back. Wings are a dark slate with a distinct edge of a lighter shade. **Whites** are pure white with orange knob, bill and shanks. Apparently this colour is very rare even in the U.S.A. where the normal African is quite popular.

Faults

The African goose is a large bird and, therefore, the criteria given for Chinese should not be applied indiscriminately. The former must possess *bulk* which is in opposition to the graceful carriage and movement of the Chinese. Nevertheless, the remarks on the head knob apply and certainly the African should not look too much like the Toulouse.

BRECON BUFF GEESE

The Brecon Buff breed was created in Wales – hence the name. It was given official recognition in the Poultry *Standards* in the year 1934 and is now kept in reasonable numbers, but is not as popular as the better known breeds such as the Embden or Toulouse.

The standard weights are 16 lb for the goose and 19 lb for the gander, but since this is a medium sized goose these weights should not be exceeded.

From a show point of view great emphasis is placed upon the colour. This should be an even buff throughout and as deep as possible. On the back, wings and thighs each feather should be laced with a lighter colour approaching white. The paunch should also be a whitish colour.

In shape there is a marked similarity to the Embden, but obviously smaller. The carriage is fairly upright with a broad body on strong, short legs. The neck is fairly long, but not as long as the Chinese goose. There is no knob, gullet or other "ornament". The plumage fits tightly around the body, again similar to the Embden.

This is a very attractive goose. It produces ample flesh on light bones and, therefore, makes an ideal table bird. Moreover, the breed is an active forager and there is generally no problem with breeding.

POMERANIAN (SADDLEBACK) GEESE

The Pomeranian goose is thought to originate from crossing the Toulouse with the Embden and then continuing to breed a distinctive species with a saddleback. The latter comes from the markings across the shoulders to the tail and top of thighs which resembles a saddle. This takes the

Figure 24.2   Pomeranian (Saddleback) Gander

198

form of mottled patches of greyish-brown (or dark-grey) across the mainly white body.

In Germany this breed has been bred for generations. They are also to be found in the U.S.A. and in Britain.

The general shape follows the Toulouse, but without the deep keel or the essential gullet. As a result the Pomeranian appears taller than the Toulouse.

There is no standard type of Pomeranian. The U.S.A. version, superficially at least, looks rather like a cross-bred Canada goose, whereas the original Pomeranian goose certainly shows the existence of Toulouse blood.

Utility Features
The Pomeranian is a hardy goose which reaches around 16 lb. It is an excellent forager and develops fast. However, in terms of laying it appears to be moderate, but nothing special. Nevertheless, many feel that this goose is worthy of more attention and official recognition by the B.W.A. could help this process.

ENGLISH GREY GOOSE

It would appear that the English Grey goose and the English White goose, traditional guardians of the farmyard, come into a similar category to the Pomeranian. They have been in existence for many generations, but their exact origin is obscure.

Some are small, compact yet plump, reaching 10-12 lb. Others are much larger and are no doubt the result of indiscriminate crossings. Once a farmer (or his wife) settles on the type he (or she) requires then they are kept indefinitely. A number are bred each year, some are eaten and the remainder are bred from; thus the cycle continues.

Figure 24.3   Sebastopol Geese

(*Photo courtesy:* Anita-Dawn Allen)

SEBASTOPOL GEESE

The Sebastopol goose is the equivalent of the Frizzle fowl in domesticated land birds. Instead of the feathers lying quite flat they curl and generally appear to be growing the wrong way. However, the feathers of the Sebastopol are not as strong as the Frizzle fowl and it has been pointed out by a number of writers that they resemble in texture the feathers of the Silkie. The latter, noted as a perpetual broody, has a sort of furry growth which, though feathers, are not properly formed, when compared with conventional breeds.

This goose appears to have originated from the area around the Danube and has been known as the Danubian goose.

In size this goose weighs between 10 lb to 14 lb. The overall colour is white and the matching colour for bill and feet are orange.

This breed suffers from two weaknesses in show birds:

1. Feathers not fully curled particularly on the breast.
2. Slipped or "oar" wing. This fault may emphasize the "wrong way" of the feathering but, of course, a physical defect should not be tolerated.

These attractive and very unusual geese are worthy of a wider following. They are easily managed.

RARE BREEDS

Breeds of geese not often seen in this country or are really ornamental waterfowl are listed below. They are included for the benefit of those fanciers who require a short account of some of the rarer species:

1. Cereopsis Goose*
The name originates from the cere which covers the bill at the base of the upper mandible; this name simply means "wax face".

The Cereopsis is rather similar to the common domestic goose of this country in terms of size and behaviour. However, it is a native of Australia and, therefore, requires adequate shelter in winter. They are excellent as table birds.

The plumage is grey-brown in colour with shoulders and tail black. The head is lighter, being a sort of grey-white. Eyes are red and the legs are a reddish colour with black feet. The incubation period is 30-35 days.

2. Gambian (Spur-Winged) Goose*
The Gambian goose has a spur on the wrist joint of the wing which it uses as a weapon. In colour it is greenish-black with a white breast and shoulders. The face and throat are a brownish-white. The bill is red and the feet a red-yellow.

These are not widely kept and are reported to be very pugnacious. Accordingly, they are best kept quite separate from other breeds as are the Egyptian geese (below).

3. Egyptian Goose*
This is the smallest and possibly one of the most ornamental of geese. Indeed in size, at around 5 lb, this goose is smaller than many ducks!

The relatively long shanks and upright carriage of the Egyptian make it appear larger than its actual size. The colour is a combination of grey, reddish-brown,

* Classified as "Ornamental"

Figure 24.4   Sebastopol and Gambian Geese
(From Wright's *New Book of Poultry*)

black and white. There is an irridescent sheen over the body making the overall effect quite beautiful. Obviously these geese are more ornamental than utility.

4. Pilgrim Geese

This is a breed developed in the U.S.A. and allows sex linkage to be practised. The originator is Oscar Grow.

In simple terms this means that at birth the sex can be seen by the colour. In the **goose** the predominant colour is light grey and in the **gander** the colour is white. Clearly this is a great advantage because any surplus ganders can be sold at an early age.

The legs and bill should be orange and the eyes are blue. A mature specimen should weigh around 14 lb.

5. American Buff Geese

The American Buffs are not standardised in Britain. In colour they are similar to the Brecon Buffs described earlier. When fully mature the goose weighs around 16 lb and the gander is 2 lb heavier. These weights are also similar to those for the Brecon Buffs officially recognized in 1934, which probably means that they preceded the American Buffs.

6. Canada Geese*

Canada geese are quite plentiful in this country. They are to be seen on lakes and large ponds in parks and similar places.

They are graceful geese of medium size (around 10 lb or a little more). The carriage is horizontal, the body is long and the breast is broad and curved. There is a smoothness of outline which puts them in a distinguished class, allowing them to compete with Chinese geese on an eye-catching basis.

*Classified as "Ornamental" by the B.W.A.

Note: There are other geese, but most of these are regarded as ornamental or fancy waterfowl, kept for their beauty rather than for utility purposes. See *Fancy Waterfowl* , Frank Finn, available from the publishers. See Colour Plate.

Figure 24.5 Group of Canada Geese   (*Photo:* Vandyck Studios)

In colour the Canada goose is dark-grey with a light grey breast and a black head and neck. On the face (at each side) is a white patch, triangular in shape.

7. Crested Geese

There are geese known as **Old English** and in the USA there is a **Tufted Roman Goose** which has a small round crest.

8. Buff Back Goose (buff head and shoulders) originating from Europe.

Figure 25.1 *Top:* How to catch a Goose: having trapped her in a
corner and grasped the neck, pick her up, encircl-
ing the wings with an arm and holding her close to
the body to avoid a blow from the wings
Bottom: Killing a Duck

Chapter 25

PREPARATION FOR TABLE

FATTENING DUCKS

The treatment of ducklings for the table is covered in Chapter 17. Basically it means giving them adequate food and water and then, by skilful management, getting them ready for killing at around 7-10 weeks depending upon the breed.

If they are kept on for breeding, ducks should be given extra food a few weeks before killing. Moreover, they may be confined to a limited space so they do not "run off" the gains in weight. At one time rice was used for fattening. This was simmered in water until quite swollen and then, after cooling, was given to the ducks. If rice can be purchased cheaply in bulk it is ideal food.

During this time green foods are essential. Cabbages and the spare leaves from lettuces can be given. A visit to the local market at closing time can often result in sacks of greens being obtained, but they should be used up before the leaves start to wither. Boiled nettles may also be mixed with the food, particularly when they are quite young.

For good digestion a supply of flint grit should be present. This is very important when ducks are confined, but if they are running in a paddock they will probably find all their requirements from foraging.

When duckling rearing was a thriving industry small straw pens or deep litter pens were used for about three weeks. This meant that at 5 weeks old the ducklings would be put into groups of around 20, all of the same size. They would be let out into a yard three times a day and fed generously, followed by a limited amount of water. Troughs were provided giving sufficient food for each duck.

Today, in commercial duck-keeping, a similar system is followed, but with the added advantage of specially formulated foods to put on maximum weight. However, it should be apparent that for the smallholder who wishes to rear 100 or so of ducks the old fashioned method is worthy of consideration. It is simple and effective and where the smallholder has the time he can mix his own foods, including the use of various wet mashes.

FATTENING GEESE

Goslings should be given high protein foods for the first few weeks and then run on grass for much of their food. However, supplementary food is advisable when natural food is in short supply or when extra intake is essential, such as when laying or being fattened.

Geese are very sociable birds and once in a social group do not like to be disturbed. Accordingly, do not attempt to fatten a goose by itself, away from its set. Separation may cause it to pine away.

Specially compounded foods such as broiler pellets may be used for fattening. Alternatively a wet mash may be given for the evening feed.

Before killing, ducks and geese should not be fed for about 12 hours. This clears the crop and avoids wasting food.

KILLING AND PLUCKING

Killing and plucking should be done fairly close together because the latter is easier when the body is still warm. Once cold, the feathers are difficult to pluck and the whole process becomes more prolonged.

Killing

Ducks may be killed quite easily by pulling the neck or by twisting it. As a rule they are no problem to handle, although the Muscovy can sometimes be difficult because the claws can be quite sharp.

Geese, on the other hand, are often difficult to catch and handle. Furthermore, if not careful the handler may receive a savage blow from the wing. If trapped in a corner a mature gander may be a formidable enemy. For this reason the correct handling is essential (*see* diagram, Figure 25.1).

Remember the goose should be killed as quickly as possible and with the minimum of pain. Methods of killing vary, but the following have been employed with success:

1. Catch the goose (*see* diagram) and tie its legs and wings firmly, then hang from a hook. Stun with a blow to the back of the head and then wring the neck. Once this is done pull the head to leave a gap into which the blood can flow and congeal.
2. As above, but kill by piercing the brain with a sharp and pointed knife either through the roof of the

209

mouth or at the base of the skull where there is a hollow.

3. Use a humane killer both for stunning the goose and actually killing. Some items of equipment use electricity for stunning and then cutting the throat. Obviously such expenditure is only worth-while if it is to be done on a commercial basis.

Irrespective of the method, do be sure to secure the goose before attempting to kill it. The wings are extremely strong and can inflict damage.

Figure 25.2 Bingham Dry Plucker

(Courtesy: Poultry World)

Plucking
Plucking, the removal of the feathers and fluff (including the difficult stubs), is an important part of duck or goose keeping. There is no point in keeping birds for the table only to find that the plucking is a task you do not wish to carry out. Yet, it has to be admitted, this process can be difficult for the amateur who has no experience.

Plucking Immediately or When Cold?
Some breeders prefer to pluck immediately a bird has been killed because the feathers are more easily removed. This is a fact which cannot be denied. However, great care must be taken not to pull too many feathers at one go or the skin will tear. There is nothing more unsightly on a bird than skin which has been pulled back to expose the flesh.

Methods of Plucking

1. **Hand Plucking**
   This means holding the bird with one hand and pulling out the feathers with the other or, for a larger bird, hanging it from a hook and then, using both hands, plucking the bird.
   There is no *perfect* way of plucking, but generally it is easier to just pluck the breast feathers, then pull out the longer feathers from the tail and wings.
   The aim is to give a smooth, clean appearance. All stubs should be removed and there should be a finishing touch added by singeing off the fluff, being careful not to blacken the skin.

2. **Dry Plucking**
   A dry-plucking machine relies on moving plates or other means to remove feathers. It is "dry" in the

211

sense of not using water in the actual operation.
Probably the best known of the dry pluckers is the
"Bingham" illustrated in Figure 25.2. This is belt
driven from an electric motor and the actual plucking is effected by holding the bird against moving
metal plates.

Alternative pluckers are the "Poultryman"
machines.

3. **Wet Plucking**

Basically this method consists of wetting the duck in
warm water and then plucking it on a machine with
rubber fingers.

This is a very efficient method, although a wetting
tank may be necessary as well as the machine. Usually this is for the large producer who is plucking
hundreds of birds per day.

4. **Wax Plucking**

Wax plucking is a method of immersing a bird in
very hot wax and then removing the feathers by
stripping off the hardened wax. Usually it involves
the following stages:

(a) Rough pluck a bird, usually by using a dry
     plucker.
(b) Dip the cool carcass in hot wax.
(c) Cool the wax by immersing in a cold bath.
(d) Strip off the feathers by pulling off the wax.
(e) Re-heat the wax and remove the feathers,
     allowing them to be sold (usually not as valu-
     able as feathers from dry plucking).

A very clean job is possible, stubs, small
feathers and fluff all being removed.

Preparation (Evisceration)
If preparation of birds is on a large scale there are special evisceration machines available. However, for the small-holder the task will have to be done by hand. It should be attempted only after all plucking and removal of stubs has been completed.
The stages are as follows:

1. **Remove Head**
   Cut neck *skin* near to head and fold back and then, with a very sharp knife, remove the neck and head from the body. This should leave a length of neck skin which covers the base of the neck removed.
2. **Take out Crop**
   The crop or food bag which is situated in the recess where the breast joins the neck should be taken out. At the same time cut around the stump of the neck to make sure it can be removed when the organs are removed.
3. **Remove Vent and Organs**
   With a sharp knife make an incision under the parson's nose and then cut out the vent at the same time, making a gap through which the heart, liver, gizzard and organs can be removed. Grasp these firmly with one hand and pull them from the body.
   The gizzard and neck, and possibly the liver, can be used for the giblets. If a bird is to be frozen it is usual to wrap the giblets in a small plastic bag and put them back into the bird.
4. **Remove Legs**
   The legs can now be cut off at or just below the hock. It may be cut at the joint which makes a very clean job or, with a sharp chopper, just below the

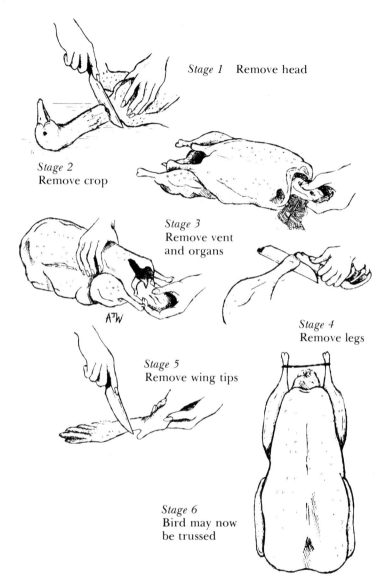

Stage 1   Remove head

Stage 2
Remove crop

Stage 3
Remove vent
and organs

Stage 4
Remove legs

Stage 5
Remove wing tips

Stage 6
Bird may now
be trussed

Figure 25.3   Preparation

joint. The latter may be preferred because the skin is then kept intact during cooking, whereas if cut at the joint the skin tends to "ride-up" when the bird is cooked.

The sinews should be removed from the legs thus making them more palatable. A simple devise called a "sinew puller" can be obtained for this purpose.

5. **Remove Wing Tips**

The ends of the wings should now be removed.

6. **Truss**

Birds may now be trussed up which involves putting string through the body and round the legs. Alternatively rubber bands may be used to position the legs and wings. If marketing on a large scale, plastic bags would be used to pack each bird individually.

An Aylesbury Drake.

215

Figure 26.1 Prizewinners – Welsh Harlequins   *(Courtesy:* Charles and Maggie Piper, Alford Acre)

Chapter 27

SHOWING

LACK OF POPULARITY

Ducks and geese have never been as popular as fowl at shows. T.W. Sturges in the first edition of *The Poultry Manual* stated that, in 1908, only 217 exhibits appeared at the International Show. Yet there were 3,500 large poultry and over 1,000 bantams. Today, more than 70 years later, similar proportions apply although usually the number of bantams predominates, these having pushed out the large fowl in terms of popularity.

The reason for the small numbers of waterfowl being shown is no doubt due to the fact that duck helpers regard their charges as *producers* – either of eggs or meat. Yet exhibiting can lead to tremendous improvements in the quality of stock. The improvements seen in the Aylesbury and Rouen are examples of what can be achieved by careful selection of breeding stock.

Preparation for show is also relatively simple. There is less fear of damaging feathers than when washing a fowl. If kept in appropriate conditions ducks or geese simply require a wash down a day or two before the show day. They are then kept on clean shavings until the feathers are dry and then taken to the show.

SPOTTING THE LIKELY WINNERS

Those fanciers who have experienced the trials of the show world will know that winners have to be spotted at an early age. An awareness of the *standard* and how the judges are interpreting the descriptions in the *standard* are essentials. Often the views of judges are at variance with the written guides. Changes take place, but the *standard* lags behind. Sometimes a judge looks for exaggerated "points" and these become the accepted norm. Provided the fashion does not result in the development of useless properties no permanent damage is done. However, if carried too far harm may be done.

With experience the likely youngsters can be spotted at an early stage. Around 6 or 7 weeks of age, those which are ahead of the others should be separated and given special food, care and attention. For table ducks the aim will be to select those with low keels and massive frames; they will grow into the ducks which achieve top weights at an early age.

Geese such as Embden or Toulouse are judged primarily on type and weight, the latter being of the utmost importance. A heavy-type goose which is undersize should never be given a top prize. Indeed, the larger the better is the criterion laid down by most judges.

TRAINING

Any bird to be shown should be reasonably tame or it will not show itself to advantage. The important principle is to keep ducks and geese tame from being quite young. Hand feeding, regular mixing with the birds at feeding time, locking up on a night and other means of getting the birds accustomed to humans will all help.

The second requirement is to pen train the birds which are to be shown. This means keeping a few show pens in a penning room. These have wire floors or wooden floors with shavings. They are fitted with water and food dishes, thus allowing conditioning food and water to be given.

Confinement should not be too prolonged or the birds will lose condition. However, carried out in small doses of a few days each the birds will become quite tame.

SHOWS AVAILABLE

Many shows are held throughout the country, particularly the main agricultural events. There is also the annual National Show held at Alexandra Palace in London in the late autumn.

At the smaller shows there will probably be a single class for ducks and another for geese. At the National Show a comprehensive classification is offered, along the following lines:

BRITISH WATERFOWL ASSOCIATION SHOW
DUCK CLASSES

Class 113 Buff Orpington Duck or Drake
Class 114 Aylesbury Duck or Drake
Class 115 Rouen Duck or Drake
Class 116 White Runner Duck or Drake
Class 117 Fawn Runner Duck or Drake
Class 118 Any other colour Runner Duck or Drake
Class 119 Cayuga Duck or Drake
Class 120 Silver Appleyard (Large) Duck or Drake
Class 121 Muscovy Duck or Drake

Class 122 Khaki Campbell Duck or Drake
Class 123 Saxony Duck or Drake
Class 124 Call Ducks, Duck or Drake
Class 125 Black East Indian Duck or Drake
Class 126 Any other variety (including ornamentals) Duck or Drake

GOOSE CLASSES

Class 127 Embden Goose or Gander
Class 128 Toulouse Goose or Gander
Class 129 African Goose or Gander
Class 130 Chinese, White or Grey, Goose or Gander
Class 131 Buff, American or Brecon, Goose or Gander
Class 132 Any other variety, (including ornamentals) Goose or Gander

Make sure entries are made on time and that they are quite accurate; otherwise there will have to be correspondence between yourself and the show secretary.

Usually cards are awarded and after judging is over these are placed on the pens. The red card denotes a First prize and at some shows special cards or rosettes are awarded for **Best of Breed** or **Best in Show**.

VALUE OF SHOWS.

Shows help the novice to make up his mind on what kind of birds he or she would like to keep. They also encourage breeders to aim for improved stock and, of course, to keep ducks and geese in top condition. Although some breeders rarely show, on balance the advantages of exhibiting certainly outweigh the disadvantages. Usually breeders who win consistently can obtain higher prices for their birds, which is a positive incentive to breed high class birds.

Figure 27.1   Goose with slipped (oar) wing

(*Photo:* Vandyck Studios)

Chapter 27

AILMENTS

HARDY CREATURES

Ducks and geese are hardy creatures. From the day they are hatched the ducklings or goslings are hardy and mature quickly. In adult life they are active, eat well and suffer from few ailments. Minor ailments can be cured, but with a serious outbreak a veterinarian should be called in. Unfortunately, when a single duck or goose collapses or goes off its food this is usually a sign that little can be done, although sometimes isolation and special food can produce results.

Recently the author was asked to advise on a goose which had lost the use of its legs and appeared to be wasting away. The poor bird was quite weak and seemed to be about to die. The dreaded Goose Influenza appeared to be the most likely illness. Fortunately the amateur's diagnosis is often wrong! As a first step the goose was hand fed with bread and milk. Within a few days it was on its feet again and eating. It appeared that the problem was simple starvation. At the time of year in question there was not enough food value in the limited grass available to maintain the body. The lesson is obvious – watch that birds always have adequate food and water, supplemented where necessary by pellets or corn, especially when grass is limited.

SUMMARY OF ILLNESSES

Some of the more common problems are summarized below:

1. **Slipped Wing**
   This is a condition where the flight feathers protrude from the side, instead of following the line of the body. Obviously the condition spoils the look of the bird, although it does not appear to affect production or breeding capabilities. The reason for the slipped wing may be faulty incubation, injury, or some genetic fault. If due to an injury then it may be safe to use an affected bird for breeding. However, if in doubt do not use stock suffering from slipped wing for breeding; the young may suffer from the same complaint.

2. **Soft Shelled Eggs**
   This is not usually a true illness, but is often a sign that a bird is too fat or is not taking grit. Supply limestone grit and watch to see if this is being taken. If the bird laying soft eggs can be detected then a "cure" may be affected by feeding it with grit, dropping pieces down its throat. Mixing with mash will also assist.

   If layers' pellets are used these will include a percentage of grit, but sometimes the content is inadequate and, therefore, should be supplemented. A special grit hopper should be kept topped up.

3. **Lameness or Bumble Foot**
   All types of poultry suffer from lameness. This may be a simple injury or an infected foot which becomes badly swollen.

Very hard ground or lack of swimming water may bring on the condition. Often the problem clears itself up. At other times the foot should be cut and the pus released. In such cases the bird should be isolated and placed on soft bedding for a day or two until the wound has healed sufficiently for walking to be resumed.

4. **Moulting**

When feathers start to fall and new ones grow this is the normal process of moulting. In itself this is not an ailment, but it can impose a strain on the bird. Moreover, a bird does not usually lay when moulting nor can it be shown.

During the moulting period the birds should be given supplementary food because extra protein is essential for growing new feathers.

5. **Worms**

Ducks and geese may suffer from worms. The usual sign is an inability to put on flesh or they fail to lay and appear "mopey".

If the grass run is affected the area should be treated with lime and rested for a period. The birds should be treated with an anti-worm remedy. The latter can be purchased from the "vet" or a specialist supplier of farm stock drugs.

6. **Goose Influenza**

This is an organism which causes a goose to lose its appetite and begin to breathe rather rapidly and with difficulty. A bird may become weak on its legs and the feathers become ruffled. Diarrhoea often occurs usually on the day before death.

Goose influenza is a killer disease. If suspected the sick birds should be isolated. There is no sure remedy, but penicillin and sulfathiazole may be effective in arresting the disease.

7. **Paratyphoid** (*Salmonella*)
Young ducks and geese suffer from paratyphoid. The organism comes in many forms. Many birds may die and the infection may spread, even to humans. Poultry may be infected from mammals such as sheep, cattle, goats, dogs and cats.

Birds affected simply stand and are quite lifeless. Feathers are ruffled and diarrhoea occurs. Ducklings may gasp for breath, tremble constantly and die slowly but surely.

Various drugs have been developed to combat the disease, but there is no certain cure. Where the disease is to be avoided there must be strict attention paid to sanitation and hygiene.

Fortunately, although this disease can have devastating effects, ducklings and goslings have built up a tremendous resistance so outbreaks are not common.

8. **Duck Virus Hepatitis**
This is a very infectious and fatal disease which occurs in young ducklings. Those affected are very weak and tend to fall about. They may sit with eyes closed until they succumb to the disease and die.

Since this is a *virus* disease it cannot be treated with antibiotics. However, a vaccine has been developed which makes the birds resistant to the disease.

BIBLIOGRAPHY

The following books were used for reference and readers wishing to study particular aspects should obtain
those in print. Those out of print may be obtained from
a second hand book dealer.

General

Anon Poultry Houses & Appliances – A DIY Guide*
Finn Frank Fancy Waterfowl*
Sheraw Darrel Successful Duck & Goose Rearing,
Stromberg, Minn. USA.
Batty Joseph Artificial Incubation & Rearing*

Books out of Print
BROWN, Edward, Races of Domestic Poultry

BROWN, J.T., Encyclopaedia of Poultry, Orme, London.
COOK, William, 4th Edition, Ducks and How to Make
    them Pay, published by the author.(C. 1895).
HICKS, J. Stephen, Encyclopaedia of Poultry, Waverley,
    London. (1908).
MACKIE, Sir Peter Jeffrey, Bart., The Keeper's Book,
    Geoarge A. Morton, Simpkin, Marshall & Co. Ltd.,
    Edinburgh and London. (1904).
*** Those marked with an asterisk(*) available from the pub-
lisher.**

OWEN, W. Powell, Duck Keeping on Money Making Lines, George Newnes Ltd., London. (1918).

STURGES, T.W., The Poultry Manual, Macdonald & Evans, London. (1909).

TEGETMEIER, W.B., The Poultry Book, George Routledge & Sons, New York. (C. 1890).

WEIR, Harrison, Our Poultry, Hutchinson, London. (1902).

WRIGHT, Lewis, New Book of Poultry, Cassell, London. (C. 1920).

INDEX

229

231